NEW EDITION

McDougal Littell

MathThematics

Teacher's Resource Book

MODULE 3 The Mystery of Blacktail Canyon

MODULE 4 Inventions

BOOK **3**

McDougal Littell
A DIVISION OF HOUGHTON MIFFLIN COMPANY
Evanston, Illinois • Boston • Dallas

Acknowledgments

Writers

The authors of *Math Thematics, Books 1–3*, wish to thank the following writers for their contributions to the *Teacher's Resource Books* for the *Math Thematics* program: **Lyle Anderson, Mary Buck, Roslyn Denny, Jean Howard, Deb Johnson, Sallie Morse, Patrick Runkel, Thomas Sanders-Garrett, Bonnie Spence, Christine Tuckerman.**

Image Credits

Photography
Front Cover © Photodisc.

Illustration
3-58 *all* Chris Costello/McDougal Littell/Houghton Mifflin Co.

All other art by McDougal Littell/Houghton Mifflin Co.

THE STEM PROJECT   *McDougal Littell Math Thematics®* is based on the field-test versions of The STEM Project curriculum. The STEM Project was supported in part by the

 NATIONAL SCIENCE FOUNDATION

under Grant No. ESI-0137682. Opinions expressed in *McDougal Littell Math Thematics®* are those of the authors and not necessarily those of the National Science Foundation.

ISBN-13: 978-0-547-00091-6
ISBN-10: 0-547-00091-X

12345678 9–BHV–11 10 09 08 07

Contents

About the Teacher's Resource Book

In conjunction with the *Math Thematics*, Book 3, Teacher's Edition, this Resource Book contains all of the teaching support that you need to teach Modules 3 and 4.

Blackline Masters

The teaching support in the Resource Books is organized by module and section and includes the following materials:

Warm-Up Exercises Each Warm-Up page is printed in large easy-to-read type and can be used to create an overhead visual or used as a hand-out. Answers for the exercises are provided at the bottom of the page.

Labsheets Blackline masters used in conjunction with various Exploration questions to present data and extend the scope of the Exploration. Answers are provided in the Teacher's Edition.

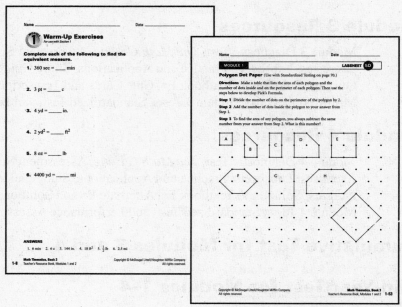

Practice and Applications One to two pages of additional practice for each section in a module, as well as combined practice that covers the whole module.

Study Guide Two to three pages of Study Guide for each section of the module. These Study Guide pages feature key concepts, worked-out examples, and exercises. They can be used for review and reteaching.

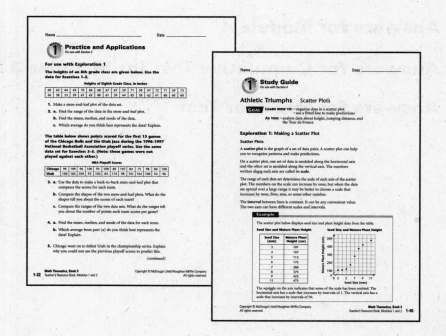

Extended Exploration (E²) Solution Guide

A comprehensive discussion of the Extended Exploration in the student textbook, including how to assess student responses and performance.

Alternate Extended Exploration (Alternate E²)

Included in the Teacher's Resource Books for Modules 2, 4, 6, and 7, these extended explorations can be substituted for ones in the student textbook. Materials include teaching notes and assessment procedures.

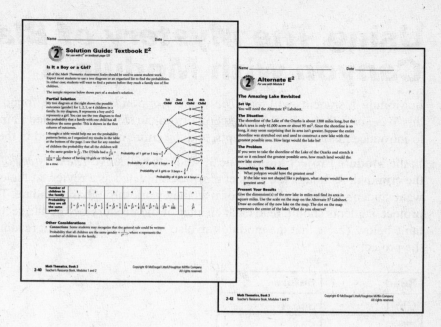

Assessment

Assessment options include a diagnostic module pre-test, quick quizzes for each section, a mid-module quiz, and two module tests, Forms A and B.

Cumulative Test

A cumulative test on both the modules of this Resource Book.

Module Standardized Test

A page of standardized multiple-choice questions for each module.

Module Performance Assessment

A Performance Assessment Task for each module.

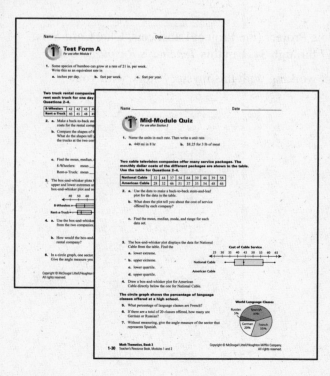

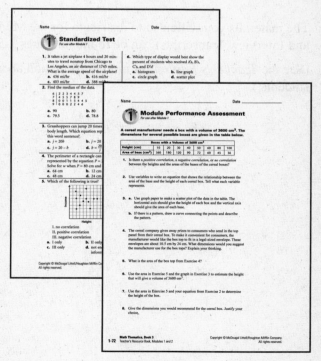

Answers

Complete answers to Practice and Applications, Study Guide, Quick Quizzes, and all Assessments for both modules are provided at the back of this Resource Book.

Using *The Mystery of Blacktail Canyon* with Module 3

In Module 3, students will read *The Mystery of Blacktail Canyon*, found on pages M-1 through M-16 in this *Teacher's Resource Book*. Excerpts from the story are included in many of the sections in the module to introduce mathematical concepts, and the entire mystery is used in the Module Project.

In the **Module Project** for Module 3, students will solve *The Mystery of Blacktail Canyon* and identify the criminal. Although the project may be completed as a review at the end of the module, you may want students to complete parts of it as they work through the module. To successfully complete the project, students should read each chapter of the mystery before the section of the module shown in the table below. (Note that the module can also be completed without reading the entire mystery or doing the project.)

Read	Before
Ch. 1	Sec. 1
Ch. 2	Sec. 2
Ch. 3	Sec. 3
Ch. 4	Sec. 4 Exp. 1
Ch. 5	Sec. 4 Exp. 2
Chs. 6 and 7	Sec. 5
Ch. 8	Sec. 6
Chs. 9 and 10	Module Project

The materials you will need to distribute for the Module Project (the Project Labsheets, Clue Card Sets, and Interview Transcripts) can be found on pages 3-57 through 3-71 in this *Teacher's Resource Book*.

(See the *Teacher's Edition* for more information about working with this mystery story with your students.)

THE MYSTERY OF BLACKTAIL CANYON

Chapter One:

ANCIENT SITES OF MYSTERY

"The thirteenth century cliff dwellings of the Anasazi were built during a long period of drought. Some scientists believe the Anasazi moved to the cliffs to escape warring tribes searching for provisions. Living on the cliffs and mesa tops was probably difficult, but the people may have felt more safe there than on the canyon floor." The speaker lifted a broken pottery bowl that had been found in the ruins of an Anasazi household.

Jim Cooper shifted in his seat to get a better look at the bowl. Jim was interested in all types of mysteries. He had come to this lecture because puzzles of the past and learning about the Anasazi had been his hobbies for years. Dr. Ashilaka, an archaeologist from Kenya, was an expert on cliff dwellings like those built by the Anasazi. Since Jim knew the area well, he hoped the archaeologist would let him help search for new sites.

"The artifacts in this display were found over eighty years ago by a young boy who had explored the cliffs and arroyos in this area." (An *arroyo* is a dry riverbed cut into rock and soil by occasional heavy rainfalls.) Dr. Ashilaka carefully placed the broken bowl on a glass case. The case was filled with many plates and bowls painted in bold patterns of black and white.

"Unfortunately, no one knows exactly where the artifacts were found," he continued. "We believe this site has yet to be discovered. The family that donated this collection helped us narrow the original location to within a twenty-mile radius of Escavada." Dr. Ashilaka maneuvered his wheelchair around the display.

"Hey, Nageela," Jim whispered.

The girl sitting next to him leaned toward him to hear his question.

"How does your dad get to the sites? I mean, with his wheelchair and all."

Nageela watched her father, remembering the fall from a cliff that had left him paralyzed. "He's been training me since he fell two years ago," she whispered back, her eyes still on her father. "I climb for him now. He calls me his 'eyes and legs.'"

She could sense Jim's admiration and was glad he was here. When she traveled with her father, she rarely met anyone her own age. Jim was 14 years old and he shared her interest in archaeology. He was a lot like her—when he saw a piece of pottery, he wondered about the life of the person who had made it.

"Most of the dwellings were built in secluded locations, with entrances that could be easily guarded," Dr. Ashilaka explained. "This makes them more difficult to find.

However, my daughter and I have completed a computer analysis of topographical maps of the area. We hope to pinpoint a site large enough to support a pueblo like the one where these pots might have come from."

Dr. Ashilaka pointed at a large aerial photo of Blacktail Canyon on the wall behind him. "A treasure found here would be priceless in terms of the knowledge of the Anasazi history and culture it could bring. Unfortunately, if thieves find the sites first, they would destroy the sites and take the treasure to a place where they could sell it illegally. Some pieces of pottery could sell for tens of thousands of dollars!"

Some people in the crowd gasped and whispered. Jim looked around the packed auditorium. He knew many of the other 22 people who had come to Escavada to hear the lecture. It seemed strange to see so many "school" faces during the summer.

His uncle, LeVerle Cooper, the science teacher at Jim's school, sat next to Gloria Blanco, the art teacher. Uncle LeVerle seemed quite interested in the topic of the lecture. The social studies teacher, Teresa Seowtewa, was taking notes for her class. Ms. Weatherwax, the principal, was also taking notes. Although she was a serious art collector, Jim was pretty sure she didn't know anything about Anasazi pottery.

Perry Martinez, Jim's mathematics teacher, was leaning against the back wall by the door. "What is he doing here?" Jim wondered. "He's never shown any interest in archaeology."

"It's almost ten o'clock." Dr. Ashilaka raised his voice to quiet the crowd. "Before we depart for the tour of the Anasazi site at Blacktail Canyon, we all need to become familiar with the area. Of course, those of you who live in Escavada probably know the canyon well, but some of us are from out of town." Nageela handed out topographical maps. Then her father compared them with the aerial photo.

There wasn't room for everyone at the lecture to go on Dr. Ashilaka's tour of the Blacktail Canyon site. Jim felt fortunate to be included, especially since the sites were used only for research and rarely open to the public. As he boarded the tour bus with the 12 others, he noticed with apprehension that the sky had clouded over.

Sure enough, almost as soon as everyone had climbed off the bus in front of the Anasazi dwellings at Blacktail Canyon, there was a torrential cloudburst. Dr. Ashilaka led them into one of the dwellings where it was dry.

"Entering a site is not a problem as long as you obey one rule." He scanned the crowd until he had everyone's attention. "Whatever you see, whatever you find—however tempting it might be—don't touch it!"

Jim noticed an opening in the back wall that led to a smaller room, possibly a storeroom. Jim asked questions about its use, but when he asked how big each room was, Dr. Ashilaka said he didn't know. "You look like an intelligent boy," he said. "You estimate the length, width, and height, and tell us what you find."

In a few minutes, Jim was back with an answer. "I know that my height and my arm span are about 5 feet. The big room is about twice my reach across the floor in both directions, and about twice my height. So, I guess it's about 10 by 10 by 10 feet. I can barely stand up in the center of the small room, and can just touch two walls. It must be about 5 by 5 by 5 feet." Jim looked puzzled. "I guess the big room is twice the size of the small one. But the funny thing is, it seems so much larger."

Dr. Ashilaka laughed and called Jim over. Nageela groaned and shook her head. She knew what was coming. She had heard the length, area, and volume lecture many times before.

Now you are ready for Section 1, Setting the Stage and Explorations 1 and 2, in your math book.

Chapter Two:

WASHOUT

"I've never seen rain come and go so fast," said Nageela, standing with Jim outside the dwelling. "I checked my watch when it started. It was just noon. It rained like a waterfall for half an hour, and then quit. It's not even one o'clock now, and everything's nearly dry."

Having lived here all his life, Jim knew the desert was a land of extremes. The ground could be completely dry for weeks. When the clouds finally came and dropped their rain, the drenching downpour became a rushing river, washing away anything in its path. Once the rain stopped, the heat of the returning sun quickly evaporated the water.

Jim laughed. "I've never seen rain any other way! Doesn't it rain in Kenya?"

As they boarded the bus and settled in for the hot drive back to Escavada, Nageela told him about the days and days of soaking rain during the monsoon season at home. Jim shook his head in disbelief.

"I went to Phoenix once," he said, "but that was the only time I've ever left the state. I'd give anything to travel like you."

Jim bombarded Nageela with questions about other archaeological sites she had explored, listening intently to her descriptions. The other riders talked quietly or dozed as the bus rumbled along the road back to Escavada. Then, suddenly, as the bus rounded a curve, the driver slammed on the brakes, jolting everyone to attention. The bus was stopped just inches in front of a small ravine about two feet deep. Though the ravine was already dry, Jim could see that ten yards of the roadway had been washed away by a flash flood.

From across the span of the washed-out road, the blue and red lights of a highway patrol car flashed. The bus driver swung the door open and stomped out. Jim and Nageela watched him through the window. He stared at the edge of the road, scratching his head, and then hopped down into the gully. On the far side, two patrol officers were inspecting a car that hadn't been as lucky as the bus. Its front tires hung over the edge of the washout.

After returning to the bus, the driver stuck his head through the door. "Might as well stretch your legs," he said. "We're not going anywhere for a while."

Everyone climbed out of the bus. There was nothing to do but wait. Jim waved at the highway patrol officers, Ferrel Yellow Robe and Charlotte Lopez. Everyone knew everyone in a small town like Escavada. Ferrel was rolling a wheel attached to a handle beside a long, black skid mark. Charlotte was busy taking notes.

"Hey, Ferrel, what's up with the car?" Jim and Nageela crossed the gash in the road.

"Hey, Jim! I should've guessed you'd show up here!" He chuckled and spoke to Nageela. "Whenever there's a mystery around here, Jim Cooper can't be far away!" Now it was Jim's turn to feel the admiring look of his new friend.

Jim smiled. "Ferrel, this is Nageela Ashilaka. Her dad's the archaeologist studying the cliff dwellings."

"Nice to meet you. What did you mean by a mystery?" Nageela asked.

"Oh, it's probably nothing," said Ferrel. "But there's something strange about this car. You see those skid marks? Whoever was driving must've been going pretty fast to skid that far, even on wet asphalt. Too bad, too. From the looks of it, the car had almost come to a stop when it dropped over the edge. If it had stopped in time, it would have saved us all a lot of work." In response to their puzzled looks, he continued. "You see, a speeding car that skids to a stop is no big deal. But look."

He motioned toward the front of the car. For the first time, Jim noticed the cracked windshield above the steering wheel. There was blood on the glass and dashboard.

"The impact probably came when the front tires dropped in the gully. So now we have an accident to investigate," said Ferrel.

"But, where is the driver?" asked Nageela, looking around.

Ferrel shrugged. "No one was here."

"Who is the driver?" asked Jim. "I don't recognize the car."

"It's a rental." Ferrel continued rolling the wheel along the skid mark made by the car. "Someone picked the car up at Crownpoint some time after 11:30."

Nageela asked about the wheel the officer was holding.

"It's a *trundle wheel*," said Ferrel. "It's used for measuring the length of skid marks. When I investigate an accident, I check the road conditions, the length of the skid, and the condition of the tire tread. There's a chart that we use to figure the speed the car was going when the driver hit the brakes, or we can plug numbers into a formula. Just routine."

"So you can tell how fast this car was going when it started to skid?"

"Well, we can get pretty close. And this car was going way too fast!"

"People who know this area well often speed along here," said Jim.

Nageela shook her head. "You'd have to be crazy to speed on a sharp curve like that!"

Charlotte laughed. "We call it *Dead Man's Curve!*"

Now you are ready for Section 2, Explorations 1 and 2, in your math book.

Chapter Three:
BIG FOOT

The two police officers called the group from the bus over to the abandoned car. "Folks, we've got a problem here," Officer Yellow Robe explained. "The driver of this car has a head injury and is missing. Now, he or she may have caught a ride back to town. It's also possible that the driver walked away dazed and may be lost, or even unconscious, in the desert. Until the search and rescue team from Crownpoint arrives, we need your help to do a systematic search of the area. Officer Lopez will explain the procedure."

As the crowd formed a circle around Officer Lopez, Ferrel pulled Jim and Nageela to one side. "Jim, I'm going to ask you to help us out. These folks can cover the immediate area, but I don't want them scrambling up the canyons. I need you to comb the back country. But be careful! I don't want to have to hunt for two victims. Which reminds me—Nageela, you stick with the rest of the group. Jim may have to do a little climbing."

"Nageela will be more helpful than you think," laughed Jim. "Besides, you know I'm not great with heights!"

"I'm an experienced climber," Nageela explained. "My father trained me."

Ferrel looked skeptical. "But you don't know the area."

"If my dad says it's okay, can I help Jim search?" she asked.

"It's okay with me," Ferrel replied.

As Nageela walked past the car, she glanced inside and then stopped. "Ferrel," she called.

"What's on the front seat?"

Ferrel wrapped his hand in a handkerchief and opened the door. He reached for a sheet of paper on the seat. It was the pamphlet from Dr. Ashilaka's leture. "Very good!" Ferrel said, "This might be a piece of helpful evidence.

"Nageela, does this area look familiar to you?" Dr. Ashilaka called from the other side of the washout.

Nageela studied her surroundings.

"Don't you recognize the terrain from the topographical maps? Our computer analysis identified this canyon as the most probable location for the cliff dwellings we are searching for."

Nageela looked from the canyon to the paper. Was it merely coincidence that the missing driver had gone to her father's lecture? A sudden feeling of urgency came over her as she and Jim hurried to the bus.

They retrieved their backpacks and water bottles from the bus. Nageela turned to her father, remembering that she needed his permission to help Jim search. Without exchanging a word, he nodded his consent. She pulled out a bandanna and rolled it into a sweat band. As she tied it at the back of her head, she searched the surrounding landscape, her excitement rising. This was what she'd been waiting for, what her father had trained her to do—to scramble and jump, to climb, to search. She picked her route and set off at a jog.

"Hey! Wait up," shouted Jim. He grabbed his pack and chased after her.

They started with the easy spots, jogging along the Blacktail Wash, a pathway packed with sand and gravel created by frequent flash floods. They checked the dozens of nameless arroyos branching out from it. The rain had covered most of the canyon bottom with fresh mud, now baked dry by the sun. Their shoes left scuff marks in the dirt. Anyone walking through it soon after the rain would have left clear footprints.

Nageela moved with confident speed over the rocks. Though Jim was more cautious, he had a feel for the land since he had hiked in the area all his life. After they had systematically combed the flats, Jim led the way into cracks and crevices further up the canyon. They explored several which turned out to be box canyons—dead-ends that led to cliffs too steep to climb. Some opened unexpectedly into broad canyons with sandy bottoms and scattered pines. Yet neither Jim nor Nageela noticed any signs of footsteps. After a frustrating hour, they returned to the car.

"Hey, Ferrel, any luck?"

"Not a thing. It just doesn't figure. I mean, what are the chances of an injured person walking away through all this mud and sand and not leaving a trace?"

"None at all," said Nageela, "unless he never left the road."

"Maybe he didn't want to be followed, so he never left the rocks," suggested Jim.

"But why wouldn't he want to be followed?" asked Ferrel.

"For tens of thousands of dollars," said Jim. Nageela nodded, remembering her father's words.

They tried several routes from the car to the rocks, but all crossed through the dirt.

"There's just no way," said Ferrel, "to get from the car to the rocks without crossing the mud somewhere. He'd have to cross the washout. I say he walked back to the highway and caught a ride to town."

"Maybe," said Jim. "But maybe we're missing something. How would a person who wants to disappear cover his tracks?"

"If this weren't a desert, I'd say through a river or creek," said Nageela. "No one can track you through water."

"That's it!" Jim jumped down into the washout. "No one could walk up this gully when the water was at its peak. But there must be a few minutes after the rain stops when the water is shallow enough to walk in, but still deep enough to wash away the prints! Then the driver could walk right up the flood channel to the rocks!"

Ferrel gave everyone instructions to spread out along the edges of the channel cut by the flood. They searched along the banks of the channel until Jim spotted a small patch of brown on a rock.

"Ferrel," he shouted excitedly. "I think I found blood!"

Ferrel examined the rock. "Good job, Jim."

But Jim and Nageela were already sprinting across the rocks, following the path the driver would have taken. It lead straight into a box canyon.

"Now what?" asked Nageela. "We just found him, and we've already lost him."

"Wait a minute," said Jim. "There's a crack here in the rocks."

Jim slipped easily between the slabs of stone and disappeared from sight. After a brief silence, Nageela heard an excited shout of joy.

"Footprints," hollered Jim. "We're on the trail!"

Nageela slipped between the rocks, followed by the two officers. They found themselves in yet another narrow canyon.

"Do you think these are the driver's footprints?" Nageela asked.

"They must be," said Ferrel. "Otherwise, the rain would have washed them away. Now we can tell how tall the driver is."

"How will you do that?" asked Jim. "All I can tell is which way the tracks are going."

"It's all right here in the sand," said Charlotte. "All you have to do is look. By the looks of the stride, this person could cover quite a bit of ground if he or she was in a hurry. If he got to the top of the canyon, he'd be back to the main road easily by now."

Now you are ready for Section 3, Explorations 1 and 2, in your math book.

Chapter Four:
CLIFF DWELLERS

Jim, Nageela, Ferrel, and Charlotte followed the tracks baked into the mud. The tracks headed straight up the canyon, as if the person knew where he was going. At first, the tracks were easy to spot in the dried mud. Jim, Nageela, and the officers were able to keep up a brisk pace. Soon, however, they were walking on solid slabs of stone. Fearing they would lose the mysterious walker, they had to slow to a cautious crawl. Then there was nothing but smooth sandstone—nothing but canyon.

"We've lost him," sighed Charlotte. "We'll have to backtrack to the last set of prints and start again."

Nageela scanned the high cliffs of the narrow canyon. "Wait a minute," she said. "We've been so busy watching the ground, we may have missed what we're looking for." She squinted, walking slowly, her eyes straining to see something in the distance. With growing excitement, she walked faster.

"Look," she shouted. "Up there!" She pointed to the top of a distant cliff.

"Do you see him? Where?" Ferrel squinted, searching the cliff. "I don't see anyone!"

"There!" Nageela pointed triumphantly at the cliff. "The computer was right!"

"What are you talking about?" asked Ferrel. "What computer? What's there?"

"You're right," shouted Jim. "I see them, too!"

"See what?"

"The cliff dwellings!" Jim was pointing up the cliff wall now.

Ferrel and Charlotte focused on the area Jim was pointing at.

"The cliff dwellings of the Anasazi," shouted Nageela. "The computer said they'd be around here, and there they are!"

"Nageela, we're hunting for an injured hiker. I don't think he'd go sightseeing in some old ruin at the top of a cliff."

"But that's exactly what he'd do," said Nageela, grinning.

"How do you know?"

"Because I don't believe in coincidence!"

While the patrol officers searched the canyon floor, Nageela and Jim ran to the base of the cliff. They searched for the toeholds used by the Anasazi to climb the cliff.

"There's some indication that he came this way," said Ferrel. "But we don't know if he went back, so we have to assume he's still up there. And if he came to steal artifacts from the dwellings, he could be dangerous."

"If he's up there and we do nothing," said Charlotte, "he'll slip away for sure. The sooner we find out, the better."

"Now hold on," said Ferrel. "We have no idea who's up there or why. There's no need to go charging up the cliffs until we can confirm that there's someone up there. And, besides, I'm not that good a climber."

"Well, don't worry about it, Ferrel." Nageela tossed her backpack on the ground. "I wasn't thinking you'd go up there in the first place. I'll be back with my gear." As she jogged away, she could hear Ferrel calling up to the cliff dwellings. Only his echo answered.

It took less than ten minutes for Nageela to reach the bus. As she clipped her flashlight to her belt and slipped on her climbing shoes, helmet, and harness, she told her father what she had seen.

"It sounds like you may have found the dwellings we're looking for!" he exclaimed. "If they have been left undisturbed . . ." Dr. Ashilaka stopped, thinking of the artifacts

Nageela might find. Then he looked worried.

"Be careful! Pay attention to how you set your bolts, and don't rush! You make mistakes when you rush. And if you see anyone up there, come right down! I mean, don't go up!" Dr. Ashilaka frowned. Nageela was afraid he had changed his mind about letting her go.

"All right," he sighed. "Do go up. But don't take chances!"

Nageela slung the heavy coil of rope over her shoulder and hugged her father. As she headed toward the canyon, she heard him call out, "And don't touch anything!"

Nageela returned with her gear to find the trio sitting on a large boulder.

"I don't know if I like this," Ferrel said, eyeing Nageela doubtfully.

"Can you tell if there's anyone up there?" Nageela asked. She meticulously checked her climbing equipment as her father had taught her.

"No," answered Charlotte. "But it seems likely that if they climbed up there to steal artifacts, they don't want to get caught. They would have left by now. Are you sure your rope is long enough?"

"No, but I'm pretty sure. How high do you think the cliff is?"

"Fifty or sixty feet."

Nageela breathed a frustrated sigh. "All right. My rope's forty meters long, and I need as much hanging down as going up. We need a better estimate than that. So how are we going to find the height of the cliff?"

Charlotte looked up at the cliff. "Hey, Ferrel. Let me borrow your pen." Without waiting, she pulled the pen out of his shirt pocket. She used her pocket knife to pry the ink cartridge out of the plastic body of the pen.

"Hang on, Charlotte! I need that," complained Ferrel.

"Not as much as we need this," she answered, holding up the empty plastic tube.

Without a word, Charlotte marked a spot on the ground, then paced off the distance to the foot of the cliff. Next, she had Jim stand between her marked spot and the cliff. Finally, she lay down with her head on the ground and sighted the top of Jim's head through the hollow pen.

"Take two steps back, Jim," she said. "Good! Now, how tall are you?"

Now you are ready for Section 4, Exploration 1, in your math book.

Chapter Five:
DISCOVERY

Once they had determined the height of the cliff, Nageela strapped on her harness. Ferrel slipped into a second harness, using his weight to anchor one end of the rope. With one step Nageela was on the cliff. She moved with skill and confidence, long legs and arms clinging to the rocks like a spider, her line tied to the harness and hanging down. At ten feet, Nageela stopped to set her first bolt. Every ten feet, she set another bolt and fastened the rope. If she fell, the closest bolt would stop her fall.

"It's a pretty easy climb," Nageela called to the others below. "There are so many toeholds and handholds that it's almost like climbing a ladder. Somebody willing to take a risk could probably do it without a rope on the first try."

At the top, Nageela silently raised herself to the edge of the cliff. Lying on her stomach, she waited, breathless. There was no sound, no movement, nothing to suggest she wasn't alone. Slowly she raised her head. As her eyes adjusted to the deep shadows in the dwelling, she gasped in horror.

"We're too late," she shouted down to the others.

"He's dead?"

"He's gone! And so are the pots!" Her experienced eye saw the signs. This had been an undisturbed site, but freshly turned dirt suggested that several pieces of pottery and many potsherds—small pieces of broken pottery—had been removed. There was nothing left but impressions in the dirt where the artifacts had been.

Down below, Jim was making his way up the cliff. He found Nageela sitting in the empty room, angry and disappointed.

"Don't touch!" she said, fuming. "Don't touch! Don't touch! All my life, that's all I've heard. I can't stand it when someone messes with a site."

"Don't worry, Nageela. We'll get the pots back."

"That's not the point," she jumped up and exclaimed to Jim. "The pots are just things! But when someone moves them, when someone steals them, we don't know where they *were*! We don't know how the people left them! We don't know anything but what they look like! Thieves don't just steal the pots; they steal what we could learn from them about the people and their lives. We'll never get that back!" She was angry that the ruins had been raided, angry that she had to tell her father they were too late. She hardly noticed Jim as he walked around the room.

"It seems about the same size as the larger room at the Blacktail ruin. In fact, it looks almost exactly the same, except for one thing." Jim walked to the back wall, where a small cave-in had left a pile of rubble up to the ceiling. He reached out and pulled on a large stone, causing the top of the pile to tumble down.

"Don't touch," yelled Nageela.

Their screams echoed down the cliff to where Ferrel and Charlotte were waiting.

"Jim! Nageela!" Ferrel shouted. "I knew this

Math Thematics, Book 3
Teacher's Resource Book, Modules 3 and 4

was a bad idea." Then he saw Jim's head appear over the edge of the cliff.

"We found it!" Jim's face was one huge dirt-smudged smile.

"Found what?"

"An Anasazi storeroom!"

Behind the pile of rubble was a storeroom, completely undisturbed, and stocked from floor to ceiling with pots, bowls, and stone tools. Nageela saw potsherds sticking out from under a pile of rocks. Then she saw what looked like bones. She scrambled like a squirrel over the top of the rubble and slid to the floor on the other side.

"Hey! Where are you going?" shouted Jim. "Don't touch, remember?"

"I'm not touching! I'm just looking, and maybe holding a little. But then I'm putting it right back!"

Jim sat on the top of the mound and watched Nageela. She stood in the center of the small room with her hands to her mouth. She didn't move or make a sound.

"I've never been the first person into a site before," she whispered, awestruck. She turned slowly, the shadows falling across her face. "I've never been the first to see. No one has lived here since—since before the pilgrims, since before Columbus. Marco Polo was probably still exploring Asia when these pots were last filled with corn."

Jim came slowly down to the floor beside her. They stood without speaking in the tiny storeroom.

Nageela finally broke the silence. "Top left: one cylindrical jar with two handles, about thirty-five centimeters high, ten centimeters in diameter. Second shelf: two seed jars, both about twenty centimeters in diameter . . . "

"What are you doing?" asked Jim.

"Taking inventory," she replied, scribbling in a small notepad she retrieved from the back pocket of her jeans. "There are over a dozen pots and platters in here, plus ladles and baskets. Before we leave, I have to record the location and approximate size of each. It's for my father."

"Everything?"

"Every pot, platter, and bowl."

"Even the broken stuff?" asked Jim, pointing to some potsherds half covered by the rubble in the doorway.

Without responding, Nageela knelt down and picked up one of the potsherds. She placed it on a patch of loose dirt and quickly traced around it with her finger. When she picked up the potsherd to put it back in its original location, Jim could see an outline of the potsherd in the dirt. Then Nageela drew a few lines on the tracing with her finger and announced, "Platter fragment on floor, original diameter about thirty centimeters."

"You mean you can tell the diameter of a platter just by tracing a little broken part? How do you do it?"

"My father taught me. It's easy, really." Nageela knelt and drew a circle with her finger. "But first you have to know a few things about circles."

Now you are ready for Section 4, Exploration 2, in your math book.

Chapter Six:
FORGOTTEN BONES

As Nageela scribbled data in her notebook, Jim wandered into another dwelling. This one was empty, as was the next one. He came back outside and knelt down to examine footprints that stopped along the edge of the canyon wall. "The driver of the car must have come this way," he said to himself. "But he didn't turn back. The footprints just stop at the wall."

"Would you stop talking to yourself and lend me a hand!" Nageela called.

As he stood, Jim reached up, his hand finding a smooth hole in the rock. He examined the wall and found more holes above and below this one. These were toeholds used by the Anasazi to climb the cliff. They probably had a field of corn growing in the flat land above the canyon wall, and would climb out each morning to tend their crop, and climb down to escape the heat of the afternoon sun. Jim realized that, once on top of the canyon, a modern road would be just a short hike across the desert.

"I think I know how the thief got out," Jim said, looking over his shoulder at Nageela who was unraveling the end of the climbing rope. "Whoa! What are you doing?"

"I didn't bring any measuring tools and Father will want to know the size of the bones. I'll cut strands of rope that equal the length and circumference of each *femur*. We can measure the strands when we get down."

"If you cut any more off of that rope, will we be able to get down?"

"We'll still have enough rope, don't worry. And we can't take the bones with us; you heard what Father said! No matter how interesting or tempting, don't touch it! Besides, it's against the law to remove anything from an antiquities site without permission. Don't forget that those are two law enforcement officers down there."

"So what's the point? What do you expect to learn from the bone measurements?"

"I don't know, but my dad will. I want to give him some evidence to analyze." Nageela shoved the pieces of rope into her pocket. "Come on, let's get going."

In the days that followed the announcement of the discovery and theft, the sleepy town of Escavada erupted into activity. Jim and Nageela provided the local police and federal agents with as much information as they could.

The police created a database listing the names, height, blood type, and alibi of everyone who attended the lecture. The police's working theory was that the thief was a local person who had attended Dr. Ashilaka's lecture. He or she was probably familiar with the back country, but ignorant of the value of Anasazi artifacts until Dr. Ashilaka revealed their potential value.

Nageela spent half a day struggling to answer her father's questions about the dwelling. Just as she was sure she had covered everything, he would ask her another question, and she would remember yet another detail. By the time the university archaeologists arrived, Dr. Ashilaka had an almost perfect map and inventory of the cliff dwelling, without ever having been there. It wasn't until the team had met, planned the excavation, and left Dr. Ashilaka and Nageela alone, that he gave her a meaningful wink.

"All right, what did you bring me?"

"Bring you? Father, you know I would never take anything from a new site!"

"Yes, I know that well. Which is why I have been so curious."

"But Father! I didn't carry anything down. I answered every question you asked. What makes you think I could have anything else for you?"

"Because you are my daughter, and I know what I would have done. So what is it?"

Nageela grinned as she pulled the strands of rope from her pocket. Dr. Ashilaka chuckled quietly, then broke into a joyous laugh.

"Tell me everything!"

Dr. Ashilaka was thrilled that Nageela had found not only a complete skeleton under the rubble, but also a partial skeleton. It was the femur from the complete one that intrigued him. Over and over, he asked her, "Are you sure this string is the length of the femur? Are you absolutely sure?"

Dr. Beatrice Leschensky, a scientist from the University of New Mexico, had been contacted by the police and was conducting the official analysis of the bones. Eager to hear her findings, Dr. Ashilaka sent Nageela to speak with her at her laboratory.

"So, your father is having a little trouble understanding the bones, eh?" She laughed easily, enjoying her old friend's frustration. "I really should just let him stew, after all of the tricks he's played on me. What I don't understand is where he gets his information! He had the measurements of those femurs accurate to half a centimeter! Who could have told him?"

Nageela turned away quickly to avoid Dr. Leschensky's eyes and bumped into a model skeleton, almost knocking it over. Then Nageela answered nervously, "He asks such good questions, he just never misses a thing!"

"Well, however he does it, I think you'll love to hear the results we have from those bones. After all, you and your friend Jim are the two who found the site!"

"We've found out a great deal about the two skeletons," continued Dr. Leschensky. "There are a couple of very old human bones, probably those of a woman. How or why her bones came to be there I don't know. The femur that puzzled your father is too large and too recent to be Anasazi. All evidence suggests it is from a Caucasian male who died in the 1800s."

"How can you tell how old the bones are?" asked Nageela.

"The police asked the same question," Dr. Leschensky said, smiling. "We know from their general appearance that they aren't recent. So we can use carbon dating, a technique used to find the approximate age of bones and fossils. Every living creature contains a certain amount of a radioactive substance known as *carbon-14*. After a plant or an animal dies, the carbon-14 decays, so that there is less and less carbon-14 over time. After about 5730 years, only half the carbon-14 remains. After another 5730 years or so, only one fourth the carbon-14 remains. After each additional 5730 years,

only half the previous amount of carbon-14 remains. By measuring the amount of carbon-14 in these bones, I was able to estimate their age. That's all there is to it."

Nageela looked confused. "So, that's all there is to it?" she sighed. "Oh, well, if that's all there is, it's as clear as . . . as clear as . . . mud!"

"Maybe I can explain it better later. Right now, you might be interested in what else we found out about the two people. We have a number of equations that help us predict the heights of people based on different bones of the body," said Dr. Leschensky. "Most often we use the femur, the tibia, the humerus, or the radius. Since we have the measurements of two femurs, we will use these equations." She erased the chalkboard and wrote two formulas on it.

Male height from femur length
$$h = 61.41 + 2.38f$$
Female height from femur length
$$h = 49.74 + 2.59f$$

"You see, h represents height and f is femur length in centimeters. The formulas depend on the type of bone as well as on the race and gender of the person. When we use the formulas, we get close to the real height, but the answer may not be exact. One of the femurs found in the cliff dwelling is 38.9 cm long; the other one is 35.6 cm long. Do you know how to use the formulas to find the heights of both people?" she asked.

"Of course," Nageela responded, "we solve formulas in school all the time."

"Well then, here is a calculator. How tall were they?"

....

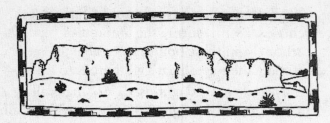

Chapter Seven:

SHADOWS IN THE SAND

A full week had passed since Nageela and Jim unveiled the Anasazi storeroom tucked into the cliff dwelling. The archaeologists had been very busy. Dr. Leschensky's guess about the larger femur was probably correct. Near where that bone was found, the archaeologists also found a few scraps of leather and a small pouch with several gold nuggets. He was possibly a prospector who never had the chance to cash in on his find. The roof probably collapsed on top of him, leaving him completely buried.

Since Dr. Ashilaka had taken charge of the excavation, Nageela had been to the cliffs every day to "be his eyes." At the end of each day, he would ask Nageela about what she had seen. He closed his eyes, envisioning every detail, until he knew the layout of the cliff dwelling better than anyone. He could say where every pot, every bone, and every tool lay.

Because it was summer, Jim was able to join Nageela in her work. They worked all day at the excavation site. In the evenings they helped Dr. Ashilaka record new data in the computer.

While their findings were exciting, they could not forget the stolen artifacts. They stopped by the police station every few days to ask about the case. Unfortunately, there was still no progress toward finding the thief who had raided the outer room of the cliff dwelling.

The center of operations for the excavation was a rented trailer on the edge of town. Late one afternoon, as Nageela and Jim sat in the shadow of the trailer discussing the theft, Ferrel Yellow Robe drove up.

"Hey, Ferrel," Jim said. "Any news on the case?"

"I just got back from Albuquerque with the data on the blood type."

"So, what are you waiting for?" Jim demanded, jumping to his feet. "Why don't you arrest somebody?"

"Hang on, Jim. We don't have enough to go on. Just a collection of circumstantial evidence."

"But what about the blood type?" Nageela stood next to Jim.

"Of the 22 people at the lecture, about half of them will have the same blood type as the thief," Ferrel explained. "It's a common blood type, type A. We need more evidence."

Jim knelt down, drawing lines with a stick in the dirt. He pointed the stick at Ferrel. "What would you say if we find a person who was at the lecture, is the right height, and is the right blood type?"

"I'd say you've found one of a dozen possible suspects."

"And what if that person has a week-old cut on his forehead?"

"I'd say we have a case. What do you know?"

"Nothing, yet."

Ferrel smiled. "I was just going to the station to enter the blood type into the database. Want to come?"

The sun hung low in the sky by the time they reached the station. The heavy ring of keys echoed down the empty stretch of road as Ferrel unlocked the station door. Here, even the police station closed at six.

"Is it always this quiet?" Nageela looked uneasily down the empty road.

Ferrel studied the small group of buildings that made up the town of Escavada. "Not usually," he replied. He ushered them into the station, checking the street once more before closing the door.

"Let's get to work," Jim urged.

"This way." Ferrel led them past the offices to a small workroom in the back. He flipped on the light and arranged three chairs in front of a computer. Ferrel entered a command and the machine hummed obediently. A list of instructions appeared on the screen.

"I know this program," said Jim, sounding surprised. "Can I try?"

Ferrel and Jim switched seats. As Jim entered commands, the screen became a list of names and numbers. "There are a lot more names here than I expected. And look." He pointed to several of the blank spaces on the screen. "There's data missing. We need to complete the database if we're going to find any answers."

"Oh, no," moaned Nageela. "Couldn't we just search what's there? It's close enough, isn't it?"

"Sure, if you don't mind the thief getting away because we don't have his height."

She sighed. "What do we have to do?"

"Grab a pencil and paper. We'll write down the missing pieces of data."

Ten minutes later, Jim and Nageela left the station.

"Well, at least we know what we're missing," Jim said as they walked along the empty street. "But how are we ever going to find out how tall Ms. Weatherwax and Mr. Martinez are?"

"Too bad we can't just ask them," Nageela said. "But if one of them is the thief, they might get suspicious and dump whatever they stole. Then we'll never prove anything."

The sun was setting as they walked past Jim's school.

"What's going on in there?" asked Nageela, nodding toward the school. Lights shone through the tall windows and spilled out of open doorways.

"A month before school starts, teachers meet with the principal each day. They talk about how they can make life difficult for us kids." Jim smiled and then became serious.

"Follow me," he said and hurried toward the school.

Jim peeked into an open doorway.

"It looks like the meeting's over," he whispered. "Ms. Weatherwax is usually the last to leave and that's her car in the parking lot."

"What are you going to do?" Nageela whispered.

"I don't know, but I'll think of something."

"Well, you'd better think fast," said Nageela. "She's turning off the lights."

One by one the windows turned to black. They heard the determined click of Ms. Weatherwax's heels on the tile floor.

"I think we'd better get out of here," whispered Nageela through clenched teeth. The cool night air made her shiver.

"I've got it," said Jim, grabbing Nageela and pulling her into the shadows. "We'll wait over here."

Just then, the door opened. Ms. Weatherwax walked quickly outside. She wore a business dress and carried a briefcase.

"Hi, Ms. Weatherwax."

The principal gasped, startled at seeing Jim appear from the shadows.

"Jim, what are you doing here?" she said, her eyes narrowing.

"Come meet someone," he said, motioning to Nageela.

Ms. Weatherwax walked over to Jim and Nageela. "You're Dr. Ashilaka's girl, aren't you," she said before Jim could introduce Nageela. It was a statement, not a question, and definitely not an opening to conversation.

"Yes." Nageela offered her hand.

"It was nice to meet you. Now, if you'll excuse me." Ms. Weatherwax turned to leave.

"Sure, only I was just wondering how you got that bump on your forehead!" said Nageela.

Ms. Weatherwax's hand shot to a yellowing bruise and scab just above her eyebrow. "I was preparing to give a lecture at a conference last week. The projection screen was stuck, so I pulled really hard. The end of the screen broke and swung down. The next thing I knew I was on the floor."

"Your audience must have thought you'd killed yourself," Jim exclaimed.

"No. I was alone, setting up early. I was . . ." she stopped abruptly. "I don't know why I'm explaining this to you two. Good-bye." She turned abruptly and hurried to her car.

Nageela and Jim watched in silence as she left.

"It's her," Jim exclaimed. "Did you see that bump on her forehead?"

"But you heard what she said. What if it's true?" Nageela sighed. "To be sure, we need her height."

"We have it," Jim said, pointing to the ground. "Look! Footprints! You can see right where she walked!"

"But the dirt's too dry! You can't make out the whole print!"

"No, but she was wearing heels. It's easy to mark exactly where each foot landed." Jim measured the distance of her stride by counting the number of times his hand-width fit between one left heel and the next—about 22 hands. As he was checking his findings, the door opened and a shadow fell across his hands. He looked up to find a man staring at him.

"Oh, hi, Mr. Martinez."

"Hey, Jim. Lose something?" Mr. Martinez walked to where Jim was, the light from the open door throwing a shadow of his large figure on the ground.

"Well, no," Jim stammered. "I was just showing Nageela how . . ."

"Jim was just explaining why the dirt is so red around here," said Nageela quickly.

"Is that right?" Mr. Martinez never took his eyes off Jim. Jim shrugged, smiling self-consciously. "Don't worry, Jim, I won't quiz you right now. But I'll be looking forward to hearing your explanation soon."

Jim looked embarrassed and scuffed his feet in the dirt.

"Well, kids, I've got to run to an appointment." Mr. Martinez lifted his thick hair off of his forehead to reveal a neat black line of stitches. "The doc's taking these stitches out for me tonight. Guess that'll teach me not to turn my back on a crowd at the rodeo. Someone knocked me over and I cracked my head. No one even noticed. I just sat there bleeding. Well, see you soon, Jim. 'Bye, Nageela."

Mr. Martinez hurried off toward town.

"Now we've really got a problem," Jim said.

"One of them may be lying about the cut," Nageela said. "Too bad we missed our chance to get Mr. Martinez's height."

"But that's not the problem! We can calculate his height exactly. I noted where he was standing and marked the length of his shadow in the dirt with my foot."

"That was quick thinking! So what's the problem?" she asked.

"What am I going to say when he asks me why the dirt is red?"

Nageela laughed. "Worry about that later. Let's work on this problem for now."

Jim knelt in the dirt to measure the distance from Mr. Martinez's footprints to the line he had drawn. "Stand right here," he said. He measured her shadow and Nageela jotted down the measurements in her notepad.

Now you are ready for Section 5, Explorations 1 and 2, in your math book.

Chapter Eight:

WHODUNIT?

The next morning, Jim and Nageela met at the police station. Even though the pace of the investigation had slowed to a standstill, they had become familiar faces at the station.

"Good news, kids." Jack Sanchez, the officer in charge of the case, greeted them. "We might have a break in the case. Early this morning, one of the cleaning staff at the school found a backpack hidden in a box of rags. The box was in a locked storage closet, and only school staff has access to the key. The backpack had potsherds in it. So far, no one has claimed the backpack."

"How did it get there? Who could have put it there?"

"Were there any fingerprints? Was there anything else in the backpack?"

Jack laughed, holding up a hand to silence the questions. "First of all, there's no proof that the potsherds came from the new site. People sometimes find this stuff just lying in the sand."

"That's true, but it seems like too much of a coincidence," said Jim. "Finding the potsherds at the school, I mean."

"That's just what I was thinking," said Nageela.

"Charlotte met federal agents at the school and they're now at the archaeological site having the evidence analyzed. She's going to call with the results." Jack read the data displayed on the computer. "What new information have you got today?"

Jack watched as Jim entered Ms. Weatherwax's and Mr. Martinez's heights in the database. Just then, the phone rang. "That must be Charlotte," said Jack.

Jim and Nageela waited breathlessly while Jack spoke with Charlotte.

"The potsherds did come from the site you found," he said, hanging up the phone. "The backpack also had a pair of sunglasses in it and a comb with black and red strands of hair." He looked at Jim. "We're going to need another column in the database."

"Hair color," Jim said. He turned to the computer. "We need to enter the hair color of every suspect."

An hour later, Jim stared in disbelief at the screen and slowly slumped in his chair.

"What is it?" asked Nageela. "What's wrong?"

"It's the numbers! They don't add up! We must have made a mistake somewhere, but where? We've been so careful!"

"Now slow down," broke in Jack Sanchez. "These data searches can be tricky. What have you got?"

"We know a lot of things about the thief," said Jim. "We know he or she has blood type A and didn't go on the field trip. We even know about how tall the thief is. My first step was to search for suspects with blood type A. The computer found 11 people who match up. But then I ran a new search to find suspects who did not go on the field trip. Now look! Twelve people! That makes a total of 23 suspects, but there are only 22 suspects in the database! And I haven't even searched for suspects with the right height or hair color yet!"

"Oh no," moaned Nageela. "You're right! We've done something wrong!"

"Looks pretty hopeless, huh?" said Jack, and then he laughed.

Nageela and Jim glared at him. "I don't see what's so funny," said Nageela. "We could lose hours, maybe days, trying to find our mistake!"

Jack tried to look serious, but he wasn't able to hide the smile in his eyes.

"All right, Jack," said Jim, studying the policeman's face. "What's the deal?"

"Let's take a close look at your data," Jack replied.

Now you are ready for Section 6 in your math book.

....

Chapter Nine:
THE MYSTERY UNRAVELS

"We've got 'em," shouted Jim. The door to the workroom swung open and Charlotte Lopez walked in followed by her partner, Ferrel Yellow Robe.

"Got who?" asked Charlotte.

"The Blacktail Canyon thief!" Nageela waved a computer printout in the air. "It was easy once we figured out how to use the database. It's this person! Or maybe this person." She frowned.

"Uh-oh," said Ferrel. "What are you going to do now?"

"Hey, Jack!" Jim threw an arm around Jack Sanchez's shoulder. "How about we just arrest the whole bunch of them?"

"Is that your solution?" laughed Jack. "Then I don't recommend law enforcement as a career choice."

"Either one of these could be the one." Charlotte was skimming the printout. "All the facts add up, but they both have an alibi with a witness. I'd say somebody's telling stories. What are you going to do?"

"You know as well as I do," Jack answered. "When you've done it all and you're still stuck, you go back and do it again, plus more."

"Oh no!" Jim and Nageela slumped into chairs, groaning.

Jack pulled some files from a drawer, laughing. "While you kids were measuring shadows, I was doing a little police work of my own." He slapped the stack of files onto the table top. "These are transcripts from some of my interviews with the suspects. If one of them is lying, we might be able to spot it here."

Now you are ready for the Module Project in your math book.

....

Chapter Ten:
LIGHTS AND SIRENS

After studying the transcripts, Nageela and Jim were convinced they knew the identity of the thief and reported their findings to Ferrel.

"I can't find anything wrong with it," Ferrel said after reading Nageela and Jim's notes and conclusions. They stood behind him, holding their breath.

"It looks good to me, too," said Charlotte. "What do you think, Jack?"

"I think . . ." Jack had been leaning back in his chair, staring out the window. He took a sip of his coffee. "I think your suspect is smart enough to guess that we're going to crack this, so I wouldn't be surprised if we're too late already. Jim, you ride with me! Nageela, you're with Ferrel and Charlotte. Let's go, people! It's lights and sirens time!"

Contents

Book 3	Teacher's Resources for Module 3

The Mystery of Blacktail Canyon

Name _____ Date _____

Module Diagnostic Test

MODULE 3

For use before Module 3

Find each value. Tell whether your answer is exact or an estimate. (Sec. 1)

1. $-\sqrt{3600}$

2. $\sqrt{\dfrac{25}{36}}$

3. $\sqrt{78}$

4. What is the value of $\dfrac{42 - 3 \cdot 2^2}{\sqrt{4 \cdot 7 + 8}}$? (Sec. 2)

   A. $\dfrac{1}{6}$ **B.** 1   **C.** 5   **D.** 26

5. Graph $y = -3x + 2$. (Sec. 2)

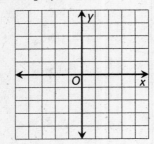

6. Which of the following equations has a graph that is nonlinear? (Sec. 2)

   A. $y = 3$ **B.** $y = 18x$ **C.** $y = \dfrac{1}{3}x + 5$ **D.** $y = 4x^2 - 7$

7. What is the slope of the line graphed at the right? (Sec. 3)

   A. $-\dfrac{1}{2}$ **B.** $\dfrac{1}{2}$

   C. 2   **D.** 4

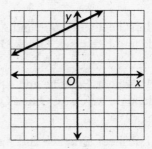

8. Choose the equation that best matches the fitted line below. (Sec. 3)

   A. $y = \dfrac{3}{4}x + 54$ **B.** $y = 3.75x - 51$

   C. $y = 3.75x$ **D.** $y = 3.75x + 51$

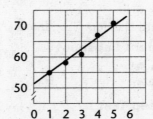

Math Thematics, Book 3
Teacher's Resource Book, Modules 3 and 4

Module Diagnostic Test
For use before Module 3

9. The flagpole in the diagram is 21 ft tall. What is the height of the tree?   (Sec. 4)

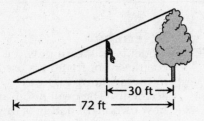

A. 15 ft   **B.** 29.4 ft   **C.** 36 ft   **D.** 50.4 ft

10. Write 5,870,000 in scientific notation.   (Sec. 5)

11. Write $6.945 \cdot 10^9$ in decimal notation.   (Sec. 5)

Solve each equation. Round decimal answers to the nearest   (Sec. 5)
hundredth and check your solutions.

12. $2.8x - 3.4 = 12.6$ **13.** $15.8 = \dfrac{y}{2.5} + 9.5$

14. Use the Venn diagram to answer the questions.   (Sec. 6)

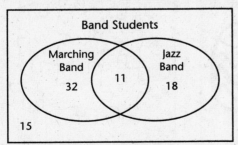

a. How many students are in jazz band?

b. How many students are in jazz band or marching band?

c. How many students are in marching band but not jazz band?

d. How many band students are not in marching band and are not in jazz band?

The Math Gazette
The Mystery of Blacktail Canyon

Sneak Preview!

Over the next several weeks in our mathematics class, we will be finding square roots, graphing equations and finding slopes of lines, recognizing and using similar triangles, writing numbers in scientific notation, and using Venn diagrams to interpret logical statements while completing a thematic unit on *The Mystery of Blacktail Canyon*. Some of the topics we will be discussing are:

► the cliff dwellings of the ancient Anasazi

► automobile skid marks

► stride length and height

► indirect measurement

► carbon-14 dating

► using a computer database

Ask Your Student

What happens to the volume of a box when you double the length, width, and height? (Sec. 1)

How can you estimate a person's height given his or her foot length? (Sec. 3)

If two triangles are similar, what do you know about their corresponding angles? (Sec. 4)

How can you tell the age of a very old bone? (Sec. 5)

Who stole the pottery from Blacktail Canyon? (Sec. 6)

Connections

Literature:
Students will read *The Mystery of Blacktail Canyon*, an original story written for this module. Students may want to read other mysteries that are set in the Southwest, such as those by Tony Hillerman.

Social Studies:
Students will learn about the landscape and people of the Four Corners region, which are central elements in the story.

Art:
Students may want to study the pottery and basket-making techniques of the Anasazi or of a modern culture. They may also want to study the designs used to decorate Anasazi pottery.

Science:
Students will learn how the coefficient of friction is used in investigating highway accidents. They will also learn how carbon-14 dating is used to estimate the age of ancient bones.

E² Project

Following Section 3, students will have about one week to complete the Extended Exploration (E^2), *Mystery State*. Students will evaluate expressions involving integers to solve a mystery puzzle. They will then create their own puzzle.

Module Project

After completing the module, students will gather clues and use the mathematics they have learned to identify the thief and write the conclusion to *The Mystery of Blacktail Canyon*.

The Mystery of Blacktail Canyon

Section Title	Mathematics Students Will Be Learning	Activities
1: Ancient Sites of Mystery	◆ finding and estimating square roots ◆ relating length, area, and volume	◆ use a map scale to estimate distances ◆ use centimeter cubes to investigate relationships among length, area, and volume
2: On the Road	◆ evaluating expressions containing square roots and fraction bars ◆ graphing equations ◆ using graphs to solve problems	◆ estimate car speeds and the length of skid marks using a nomogram and equations ◆ graph linear and nonlinear equations
3: Big Foot	◆ finding the slopes of linear graphs ◆ using equations and graphs to model situations ◆ finding the equation of a fitted line and using it to make predictions	◆ compare walking rates ◆ estimate heights from foot lengths
4: Cliff Dwellers	◆ applying the properties of similar figures including similar triangles ◆ solving indirect measurement problems ◆ constructing the perpendicular bisector of a chord of a circle	◆ use paperfolding to bisect chords of a circle and locate the center of the circle
5: Forgotten Bones	◆ writing large numbers in decimal and scientific notation ◆ solving equations involving decimals	◆ estimate ages of bones ◆ estimate heights from the measurements of bones
6: Whodunit?	◆ interpreting statements with *and*, *or*, or *not* ◆ organizing information in Venn diagrams	◆ analyze clues in a mystery

Activities to do at Home

◆ Practice estimating the number of car lengths between your car and the one ahead of it while riding around town. (After Sec. 2)

◆ Experiment with friction of a moving object on various surfaces. (After Sec. 2)

◆ Estimate the height of tall objects around your home. Then check your estimate using indirect measurement. (After Sec. 4)

Related Topics

You may want to discuss these related topics with your student:

Native American history before Columbus

Modern crime prevention and detection methods

a + b = c Careers that use mathematics and logic to solve problems

Teacher Assessment Scales

For use with Module 3

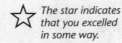

The star indicates that you excelled in some way.

 Problem Solving

❶ ❷ ❸ ❹ ❺

❶ You did not understand the problem well enough to get started or you did not show any work.

❸ You understood the problem well enough to make a plan and to work toward a solution.

❺ You made a plan, you used it to solve the problem, and you verified your solution.

 Mathematical Language

❶ ❷ ❸ ❹ ❺

❶ You did not use any mathematical vocabulary or symbols, or you did not use them correctly, or your use was not appropriate.

❸ You used appropriate mathematical language, but the way it was used was not always correct or other terms and symbols were needed.

❺ You used mathematical language that was correct and appropriate to make your meaning clear.

 Representations

❶ ❷ ❸ ❹ ❺

❶ You did not use any representations such as equations, tables, graphs, or diagrams to help solve the problem or explain your solution.

❸ You made appropriate representations to help solve the problem or help you explain your solution, but they were not always correct or other representations were needed.

❺ You used appropriate and correct representations to solve the problem or explain your solution.

 Connections

❶ ❷ ❸ ❹ ❺

❶ You attempted or solved the problem and then stopped.

❸ You found patterns and used them to extend the solution to other cases, or you recognized that this problem relates to other problems, mathematical ideas, or applications.

❺ You extended the ideas in the solution to the general case, or you showed how this problem relates to other problems, mathematical ideas, or applications.

 Presentation

❶ ❷ ❸ ❹ ❺

❶ The presentation of your solution and reasoning is unclear to others.

❸ The presentation of your solution and reasoning is clear in most places, but others may have trouble understanding parts of it.

❺ The presentation of your solution and reasoning is clear and can be understood by others.

Content Used: _____   **Computational Errors:**   Yes ☐ No ☐

Notes on Errors: _____

Name _____   Problem _____

Student Self-Assessment Scales
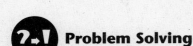

For use with Module 3

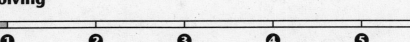 *If your score is in the shaded area, explain why on the back of this sheet and stop.*   ☆ *The star indicates that you excelled in some way.*

Problem Solving

❶   ❷   ❸   ❹   ❺

I did not understand the problem well enough to get started or I did not show any work.

I understood the problem well enough to make a plan and to work toward a solution.

I made a plan, I used it to solve the problem, and I verified my solution.

 ## Mathematical Language

❶   ❷   ❸   ❹   ❺

I did not use any mathematical vocabulary or symbols, or I did not use them correctly, or my use was not appropriate.

I used appropriate mathematical language, but the way it was used was not always correct or other terms and symbols were needed.

I used mathematical language that was correct and appropriate to make my meaning clear.

Representations

❶   ❷   ❸   ❹   ❺

I did not use any representations such as equations, tables, graphs, or diagrams to help solve the problem or explain my solution.

I made appropriate representations to help solve the problem or help me explain my solution, but they were not always correct or other representations were needed.

I used appropriate and correct representations to solve the problem or explain my solution.

 ## Connections

❶   ❷   ❸   ❹   ❺

I attempted or solved the problem and then stopped.

I found patterns and used them to extend the solution to other cases, or I recognized that this problem relates to other problems, mathematical ideas, or applications.

I extended the ideas in the solution to the general case, or I showed how this problem relates to other problems, mathematical ideas, or applications.

 ## Presentation

❶   ❷   ❸   ❹   ❺

The presentation of my solution and reasoning is unclear to others.

The presentation of my solution and reasoning is clear in most places, but others may have trouble understanding parts of it.

The presentation of my solution and reasoning is clear and can be understood by others.

Math Thematics, Book 3
Teacher's Resource Book, Modules 3 and 4   **3-7**

Warm-Up Exercises
For use with Section 1

Use mental math to find each value.

1. 5^2

2. 12^2

3. $(-3)^2$

4. $\left(\dfrac{1}{2}\right)^2$

5. 4^3

ANSWERS

1. 25   2. 144   3. 9   4. $\dfrac{1}{4}$ 5. 64

Math Thematics, Book 3
Teacher's Resource Book, Modules 3 and 4

Name _____   Date _____

Practice and Applications
For use with Section 1

For use with Exploration 1

Use mental math to find each value.

1. $\sqrt{64}$ **2.** $-\sqrt{81}$ **3.** $\sqrt{2500}$

4. $\sqrt{0.01}$ **5.** $\sqrt{\dfrac{36}{49}}$ **6.** $-\sqrt{16{,}000{,}000}$

7. The dimensions of a typical front page newspaper screen are 34 cm by 56 cm.

     a. What is the area of the front page?

     b. Suppose a square piece of paper has the same area. Estimate the dimensions of the paper to the nearest centimeter.

8. Use the sketch of the building plan for each of the following.

     a. Find the perimeter of the storage building.

     b. Find the area of the storage building.

     c. Find the area surrounding the storage building.

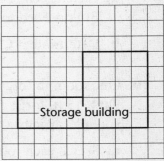

1 unit of length = 3 yd

Estimate each square root to the nearest tenth.

9. $\sqrt{42}$ **10.** $\sqrt{71}$ **11.** $\sqrt{8}$ **12.** $\sqrt{150}$

13. A square television screen covers an area of about 41 in.^{2} Estimate the length of a side of the screen.

14. What whole numbers can you substitute for n to make the statement $12 < \sqrt{n} < 13$ true?

15. **Probability** A lottery game includes numbers 1–54. What is the probability that a number picked at random for the game is a perfect square?

16. **Fill in the Blank** If the square of a number is between 25 and 49, then the number is between __?__ and __?__.

(continued)

Practice and Applications
For use with Section 1

For use with Exploration 2

17. Writing Refer to the figure in Exercise 8. A home-owner estimates that the cost of installing sod on his lot is $4 per square yard less than installing a floor in his storage building. Explain why you think this is true or not true.

For Exercises 18–19, use the equation C = 10a + 3000, where C is the cooling capacity in Btu's of an air conditioner and a is the area in square feet of the room it is cooling.

18. A two-room apartment has rooms with dimensions 12 ft × 16 ft and 10 ft × 14 ft. Chris bought an air conditioner rated at 10,000 Btu.

   a. Sketch each room. Label the dimensions. Then find the required Btu's needed for each room.

   b. Determine if Chris bought the correct size air conditioner.

19. One room in Jorge's house is 18 ft × 26 ft, and another room is 9 ft × 13 ft. Jorge estimates that the larger room needs twice as much cooling capacity as the smaller room.

   a. Sketch each room. Label the dimensions.

   b. Do you think Jorge is correct? Explain.

20. a. Find the volume of the box at the right.

   b. Give the dimensions of another box with the same volume.

   c. Challenge Give the dimensions of a cube with the same volume.

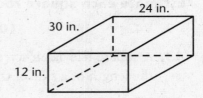

21. a. Find the volume of a cube with sides 16 in. and of a rectangular prism with sides 8 in. × 16 in. × 32 in.

   b. Compare the amount of cardboard needed to make each box in part (a).

   c. What can be said about the amount of cardboard needed to make a cubical box compared to the amount of cardboard needed to make a second box with the same volume?

Math Thematics, Book 3
Teacher's Resource Book, Modules 3 and 4

Name _____   Date _____   3-11

 **Study Guide**
For use wih Section 1

Ancient Sites of Mystery   Square Roots and Measurement

GOAL   **LEARN HOW TO:** • find and estimate square roots
                      • describe patterns related to length, area, and volume
        AS YOU: • find dimensions of a room at an archaeological site
                      • compare dimensions of rooms at an archaeological site

Exploration 1: Finding Square Roots

Squares and Square Roots

One of two equal factors of a number is a **square root** of that number.
If $A = s^2$, then s is a square root of A. Every positive number has both a
positive and a negative square root. The **principal square root**, indicated
by $\sqrt{}$, is the positive square root. The negative square root is indicated
by $-\sqrt{}$. A number is a **perfect square** if its principal square root is a
whole number.

Example
Find the square roots of 225.
Sample Response
Since $(-15)^2 = 225$ and $15^2 = 225$, -15 and 15 are the square roots of 225.

Example
Is 220 a perfect square? Explain.
Sample Response
No; $14^2 = 196$ and $15^2 = 225$, so 220 is not a perfect square because its square root is not a whole number.

Example
Find $-\sqrt{100}$ and $\sqrt{100}$.
Sample Response
$-\sqrt{100} = -10$ and $\sqrt{100} = 10$

Study Guide

For use with Section 1

Estimating Square Roots

You can estimate a square root by using a calculator, or by looking for the closest perfect squares less than and greater than the number.

Example

Estimate $\sqrt{20}$.

Sample Response

The closest perfect squares less than 20 and greater than 20 are 16 and 25.
$$\sqrt{16} < \sqrt{20} < \sqrt{25}, \text{ or } 4 < \sqrt{20} < 5$$
So, $\sqrt{20} \approx 4.5$.   Note, however, that $(4.5)^2 = 20.25$ and $20 < 20.25$.

Then, $\sqrt{20} < 4.5$ and $\sqrt{20}$ is closer to 4 than to 5.

Exploration 2: Length, Area, and Volume

Changing Dimensions

A *cube* is a rectangular prism with six square *faces*. It also has 12 *edges*.

When you compare sizes of objects, you need to know whether you are comparing lengths, areas, or volumes.

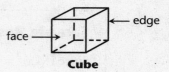

Example

Suppose the length, width, and height of the prism at the right are each multiplied by 2. Describe how this changes the areas of the faces and the volume of the prism.

4 cm
3 cm
6 cm

Sample Response

The areas of faces of the given prism are 12 cm², 12 cm², 18 cm², 18 cm², 24 cm², and 24 cm².

The areas of faces of the new prism are 48 cm², 48 cm², 72 cm², 72 cm², 96 cm², and 96 cm².

The volume of the given prism is 72 cm³. The volume of this new prism is 576 cm³.

So, the area of each of the faces of the new prism is 4 times the area of the faces of the given prism, and the volume of the new prism is 8 times the volume of the given prism.

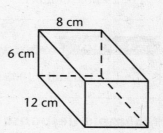

8 cm
6 cm
12 cm

Study Guide: Practice & Application Exercises

For use with Section 1

Exploration 1

Use mental math to find each value.

1. $\sqrt{360{,}000}$

2. $-\sqrt{64}$

3. $\sqrt{\dfrac{1}{25}}$

4. $\sqrt{0.04}$

5. $\sqrt{0.000081}$

6. $\sqrt{4900}$

7. $\sqrt{0.0009}$

8. $\sqrt{\dfrac{9}{16}}$

Estimate each square root to the nearest tenth.

9. $\sqrt{37}$

10. $\sqrt{24}$

11. $\sqrt{143}$

12. $\sqrt{133}$

13. $\sqrt{103}$

14. $\sqrt{228}$

15. $\sqrt{35}$

16. $\sqrt{2}$

Find each value. Tell whether your answer is exact or an estimate.

17. $\sqrt{0.0025}$

18. $\sqrt{36.4}$

19. $-\sqrt{900}$

Exploration 2

20. The volume of a cube is 27 cm^3. What will its volume be if each of its edge lengths are multiplied by 3?

21. A department store offers free gift-wrapping services for items purchased at the store. Gift boxes are available in small and large sizes.

    a. Compare the amount of wrapping paper needed to wrap each gift box. About how many times as much wrapping paper is needed for the large gift box?

    b. The volume of the large gift box is about how many times the volume of the small gift box?

    c. Not including the bow, what length of ribbon will be needed to tie around a large gift box? a small gift box?

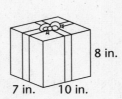

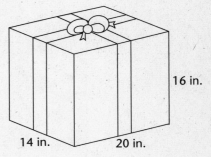

Quick Quiz
For use after Section 1

Use mental math to find each value.

1. $\sqrt{36}$

2. $-\sqrt{100}$

Estimate each square root to the nearest tenth.

3. $\sqrt{48}$

4. $\sqrt{14}$

5. A town square has an area of 1400 ft². Estimate the dimensions.

Warm-Up Exercises

For use with Section 2

Evaluate each expression.

1. $3(5 + 12)$

2. $7 - 2^3$

3. $\dfrac{4 + 6}{2}$

Evaluate each expression when $x = 2$ and $y = -3$.

4. $x + 3 \div y$

5. $2y^2 - 3 \cdot 5$

ANSWERS

1. 51   2. −1   3. 5   4. 1   5. 3

MODULE 3   LABSHEET **2A**

Nomogram   (Use with Questions 3–6 on page 169, Question 11 on page 171, Question 18(d) on page 174, and Exercise 34(b) on page 178.)

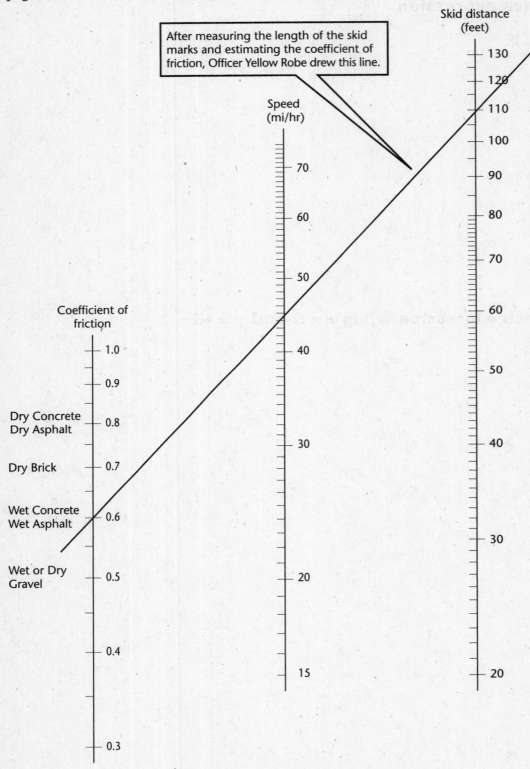

After measuring the length of the skid marks and estimating the coefficient of friction, Officer Yellow Robe drew this line.

Skid distance (feet)

Speed (mi/hr)

Coefficient of friction

Math Thematics, Book 3
Teacher's Resource Book, Modules 3 and 4

Name _____   Date _____   3-17

 Practice and Applications
For use with Section 2

For use with Exploration 1

Evaluate each expression. Round decimals to the nearest hundredth.

1. $\dfrac{2 \cdot 9}{6 - 3}$

2. $\dfrac{3(8 - 2)}{2}$

3. $\dfrac{(-6)^2}{14 - 2 - (3 \cdot 2)}$

4. $5\sqrt{3} \cdot 7$

5. $-\sqrt{12 \cdot 3} + 5$

6. $\dfrac{\sqrt{8 + 2} + 1}{3}$

For Exercises 7–10, evaluate each expression.

7. $3\sqrt{4^2 - 12}$

8. $\dfrac{12 - 7}{-4(2)^3}$

9. $6\sqrt{\dfrac{25}{3^2 - 4}}$

10. $8 + 3\sqrt{4 \cdot 2}$

11. The length of the shoreline of Keeler Lake is about 32 miles, and its surface area is about 14 mi^2.

   a. Evaluate the expression $\dfrac{L}{2\sqrt{\pi A}}$, where L is the length of the shoreline in miles and A is the surface area of the lake in square miles.

   b. Compare your value in part (a) with the value 1. The closer the value is to 1, the more circular the lake. Do you think Keeler Lake is circular? Explain.

   c. Suppose a lake is perfectly circular and has a diameter of 18 miles. Evaluate the expression for this lake. Will the value be the same for any circular lake? Explain.

Evaluate each expression when $m = 4$ and $n = -3$. Round decimal answers to the nearest hundredth.

12. $5\sqrt{m + n}$

13. $\dfrac{6m + n}{3}$

14. $\dfrac{m^3}{n}$

15. $\dfrac{m^2 + mn}{2mn}$

16. $\dfrac{25n}{2 \cdot 3}$

17. $\dfrac{\sqrt{m^2 - 4mn}}{2n}$

18. Write a numerical expression that equals 6. Your expression should include a fraction bar, a $\sqrt{}$ symbol, and at least three different numerical operations.

(continued)

Name _____   Date _____

Practice and Applications
For use with Section 2

For use with Exploration 2

19. The recommended "following distance" for a car is given by $d = 1.5s$, where d is the recommended following distance in feet and s is the speed of the car in miles per hour.

    a. Find the recommended following distance for a car traveling at 25 mi/hr.

    b. If the recommended following distance is 80 ft, how fast is the car traveling?

20. a. Estimate the speed of a car that leaves a 20 ft skid mark on a road with a coefficient of friction 0.81. Use the formula $s = 5.5\sqrt{d \cdot f}$, where d is the length of the skid mark in feet and f is the coefficient of friction.

    b. Use a graphing calculator to graph the equation $y = 5.5\sqrt{0.81x}$, where 0.81 is the coefficient of friction for dry concrete.

    c. Use your answer to part (b) to estimate the speed of a car that leaves a 50 ft skid mark.

Graph each equation.

21. $y = 3x - 1$ **22.** $y = -4x$ **23.** $y = 2x - 4$

24. $y = 6$ **25.** $y = 20 + x$ **26.** $y = 30 - x$

Graphing Calculator Graph each equation. Tell whether the graph is *linear* or *nonlinear*.

27. $y = \sqrt{x}$ **28.** $y = -0.2x$ **29.** $y = 2x^2$

30. $y = \frac{1}{x}$ **31.** $y = \sqrt{5} + x$ **32.** $y = x^3$

Math Thematics, Book 3
Teacher's Resource Book, Modules 3 and 4

Name _____   Date _____

 **Study Guide**
For use with Section 2

On the Road   Equations and Graphs

GOAL **LEARN HOW TO:** • evaluate expressions with square roots and fraction bars
• graph equations

AS YOU: • estimate speeds of cars involved in accidents
• investigate highway safety issues

Exploration 1: Order of Operations

The order of operations is a set of rules for evaluating an expression
so that the expression has only one value.

First   Perform all calculations inside grouping symbols. Grouping
symbols include parentheses, fraction bars, and square root
symbols.

Next   Evaluate any powers.

Next   Perform multiplications and divisions in order from left to right.

Then   Perform additions and subtractions in order from left to right.

Example

Simplify $\dfrac{\sqrt{6+3}}{6+3 \cdot 4^2}$.

Sample Response

When an expression has a fraction bar, simplify the numerator and the denominator
as much as possible.

First Do the addition inside the square root symbol,
and evaluate the square root.

$$\dfrac{\sqrt{6+3}}{6+3 \cdot 4^2} = \dfrac{\sqrt{9}}{6+3 \cdot 4^2}$$

$$= \dfrac{3}{6+3 \cdot 4^2}$$

Next Simplify the power, 4^2, and evaluate the product.

$$= \dfrac{3}{6+3 \cdot 16}$$

$$= \dfrac{3}{6+48}$$

Then Find the sum in the denominator, and simplify
the resulting fraction.

$$= \dfrac{3}{54}$$

$$= \dfrac{1}{18}$$

Math Thematics, Book 3

Name _____   Date _____

Study Guide
For use with Section 2

Exploration 2: Graphing Equations

An ordered pair of numbers that make an equation with two variables
true is a **solution of the equation**. The graph of an equation includes all
possible solutions of the equation. When the graph of an equation is a
straight line, the graph and the equation are called **linear**. Graphs and
equations that do not make a straight line are called **nonlinear**.

Example

Graph the equation $y = 2x - 1$. Tell whether the graph is *linear* or *nonlinear*.

Sample Response

First Make a table of values (solutions). Include several values so the pattern in the
plotted points can be seen. Be sure to include both positive and negative values
for x.

x	y	(x, y)
−1	−3	(−1, −3)
0	−1	(0, −1)
1	1	(1, 1)
2	3	(2, 3)

Then Plot the ordered pairs on a coordinate grid. The points lie along a line. Draw a
line to show the pattern. Use arrowheads to show that the graph extends.

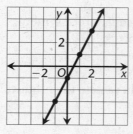

The equation is linear because its graph is a straight line.

Math Thematics, Book 3
Teacher's Resource Book, Modules 3 and 4

Name _____   Date _____

Study Guide: Practice & Application Exercises
For use with Section 2

Exploration 1

Evaluate each expression. Round decimal answers to the nearest hundredth.

1. $\dfrac{4 \cdot 2}{3 + 7 - 3(2)}$

2. $2 + 3\sqrt{2 \cdot 8}$

3. $\dfrac{\sqrt{12} + 6}{5}$

4. $(4 + 6)\sqrt{4(13)}$

5. $24 - 3(2)$

6. $\sqrt{\dfrac{8}{19 - 3}}$

Evaluate each expression when *f* = –2 and *g* = 5. Round decimal answers to the nearest hundredth.

7. $\dfrac{3 - 5f}{2g}$

8. $\dfrac{\sqrt{g^2 - 3}}{g - f}$

9. $\dfrac{-4f}{9 + g} - g$

Exercises 10–13 show the incorrect answers a student gave on a quiz. Describe the mistakes the student made.

10. $5 \cdot 10 + 1 \cdot 2 = 110$

11. $(2 + 4)^2 = 20$

12. $\dfrac{\sqrt{25 - 16}}{3} = \dfrac{1}{3}$

13. $11 - 6 \div 2 = \dfrac{5}{2}$

Exploration 2

For Exercises 14–16, graph each equation.

14. $y = 5x$

15. $y = -2x - 3$

16. $y = x - 3$

17. For which equation(s) in Exercises 14–16 is (0, –3) a solution?

18. For which equation(s) in Exercises 14–16 is (–1, –5) a solution?

19. For which equation(s) in Exercises 14–16 is (4, 1) a solution?

Graphing Calculator Graph each equation. Tell whether the graph is *linear* or *nonlinear*.

20. $y = x^2$

21. $y = 2.5x + 1$

22. $y = |x|$

Name _____   Date _____

Quick Quiz
For use after Section 2

Evaluate each expression. Round decimals to the nearest hundredth.

1. $\dfrac{(-8)^2}{6 \cdot 4}$

2. $\dfrac{-\sqrt{49} - 1}{2}$

3. Evaluate $\dfrac{\sqrt{b^2 - 4a}}{2a}$ when $b = 4$ and $a = 1$. Round to the nearest hundredth.

4. Graph $y = -2x + 3$.

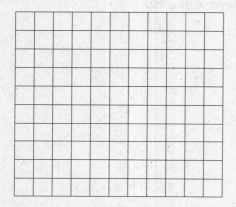

5. Tell whether the graph of $y = \sqrt{x} - 6$ is *linear* or *nonlinear*.

Name _____   Date _____   **3-23**

Warm-Up Exercises
For use with Section 3

Decide whether the point (–2, 3) lies on each line.

1. $y = 5x + 7$

2. $y = -x + 1$

3. $y = 2x - 8$

Find the values of *y* when *x* = –1, 0, and 2.

4. $y = 15x$

5. $y = 4x - 11$

ANSWERS

1. No.   2. Yes.   3. No.   4. –15, 0, 30   5. –15, –11, –3

MODULE 3   **LABSHEET** 3A

Foot Length and Height Table (Use with Questions 12–14 on page 184.)

Directions

• Measure the height and foot length (with shoes on) of each person in your group to the nearest half centimeter. Record your data in the table below.

• Exchange data with another group and record the new group's data in the table below.

• Use graph paper to make a scatter plot. Include all the data in the table. Put foot length on the horizontal axis and height on the vertical axis.

• Draw a fitted line.

Name	Foot length (cm)	Height (cm)
Adult 1	29.0	178.0
Adult 2	30.0	177.0
Adult 3	29.4	175.0
Adult 4	29.0	175.0
Adult 5	30.0	178.0
Adult 6	28.0	172.5
Adult 7	26.5	164.5
Adult 8	27.0	165.5
Adult 9	27.0	169.0
Adult 10	26.5	160.0

Sample data

Record your group's data here.

Record data from another group here.

Math Thematics, Book 3
Teacher's Resource Book, Modules 3 and 4

Name _____   Date _____

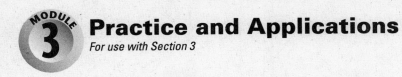

Practice and Applications
For use with Section 3

For use with Exploration 1

Find the slope of each line.

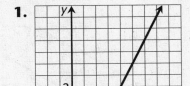

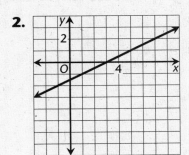

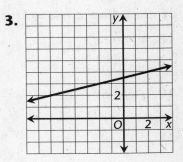

**For Exercises 4 and 5, use the graph at the right. The
graph models Juan's average Calorie usage while jogging.**

4. **a.** Find the slope of the line.

   b. Find the average number of Calories used per minute.

   c. Write an equation that you can use to find the average
   number of Calories used per minute.

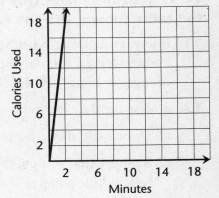

5. **a.** For Exercise (4), suppose Juan increases the number
   of Calories he uses while jogging by 10%. Write a new
   equation to model the number of Calories he uses.

   b. Graph the new equation. Find the slope of the graph.

6. **a.** On a coordinate grid, graph the points (–4, 2) and (4, 6).

   b. Draw a line connecting the points.

   c. Find the slope of the line.

   d. Explain how to find the slope of the line connecting two points.

7. **Challenge** Find the slope of a line that passes through the points
   (–3, 6) and (0, 4) without graphing.

(continued)

3 Practice and Applications

For use with Section 3

For use with Exploration 2

Match each equation with its graph. State where the graph of each line crosses the *y*-axis.

8. $y = 0.6x$

9. $y = 0.6x - 4$

10. $y = 0.6x + 4$

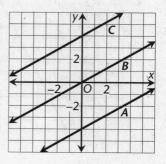

Health **The average remaining life expectancy for 11–17-year-old males (for their age in 1991) is given in the table shown. Use the table for Exercises 11–12.**

Age	Years
11	62.0
12	61.0
13	60.0
14	59.0
15	58.1
16	57.1
17	56.2

11. **Interpreting Data** What does the table show about how, on the average, the remaining life expectancy for males changes as males get older?

12. a. Use the data in Exercise 11 to make a scatter plot.

b. Draw a fitted line for the graph. Then find its slope.

c. Suppose that you guess that the equation for your fitted line follows this pattern:
   Remaining years = 73 – slope × current age
Write an equation for your fitted data based on this pattern.

d. Use your equation in part (c) to predict the remaining life expectancy for a 21-year-old male as of 1991.

e. The actual answer to part (d) was 52.5 years. How does your answer in part (d) compare?

Math Thematics, Book 3
Teacher's Resource Book, Modules 3 and 4

Name _____ Date _____

Study Guide
For use with Section 3

Big Foot   Slope and Equations

GOAL **LEARN HOW TO:** • find the slope of a line
• use equations and graphs to model situations
• use an equation to make a prediction

AS YOU: • compare walking rates
• estimate heights from foot lengths

Exploration 1: Finding Slope

The **slope** of a line is the ratio of its vertical change, **rise**, to its horizontal change, **run**. Slope is a ratio that measures the steepness of a line.

$$\text{slope} = \frac{\text{rise}}{\text{run}}$$

> **Example**
>
> Find the slope of the line in the graph below.
>
> **Sample Response**
>
>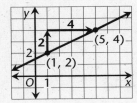
>
> The vertical change (rise) is $4 - 2$, or **2**.
>
> The horizontal change (run) is $5 - 1$, or **4**.
>
> Therefore, the slope is $\frac{2}{4}$, or $\frac{1}{2}$.

Exploration 2: Using Equations

You can use an equation of a fitted line to make predictions.

> **Example**
>
> An equation of the fitted line on a scatter plot is $t = c + 40$, where t = temperature in degrees Fahrenheit and c = number of chirps a cricket makes in 15 sec. What can you predict about the temperature if you hear a cricket chirp 10 times in 15 sec?
>
> **Sample Response**
>
> Evaluate the equation when $c = 10$.
>
> $t = c + 40 = 10 + 40 = 50$
>
> If you hear a cricket chirp 10 times in 15 sec, the temperature is about 50°F.

Name _____   Date _____

Study Guide: Practice & Application Exercises

For use with Section 3

Exploration 1

Find the slope of each line.

1.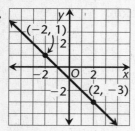

2.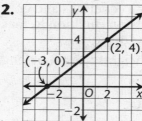

3. The graph below models Tristan's average typing rate.

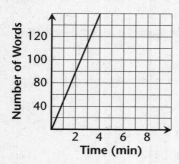

a. How many words does Tristan type per minute?

b. Write an equation for the number of words he types based on the number of minutes he types.

c. Suppose Tristan learns to type 5% faster. Write a new equation to model his typing rate.

Exploration 2

The scatter plot at the right shows the number of hits and the number of times at bat for members of a baseball team. Use the scatter plot for Exercises 4–6.

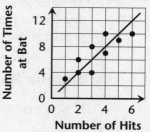

Batting Statistics for a Baseball Team

4. Predict the number of times a batter will get a hit in 6 times at bat.

5. Find the slope of the fitted line.

6. Let t = the number of times at bat and let h = the number of hits. Which equation can you use to predict the number of hits if you know the number of times at bat?

A. $t = 2h + 1$ **B.** $t = \frac{1}{2}h$ **C.** $t = 2h$ **D.** $t = \frac{1}{2}h - 1$

Math Thematics, Book 3
Teacher's Resource Book, Modules 3 and 4

Quick Quiz

For use after Section 3

1. Find the slope of the line.

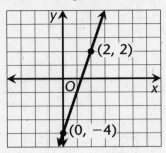

Match each equation with one of the lines. Explain your thinking.

2. $y = 2x$

3. $y = 2x + 3$

4. $y = 2x - 3$

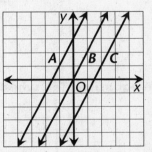

Name _____ Date _____

Mid-Module Quiz

For use after Section 3

Find each value. Tell whether your answer is exact or an estimate.

1. $\sqrt{0.25}$

2. $\sqrt{400}$

3. $-\sqrt{120}$

4. Candice estimated that the larger cube will hold 9 of the smaller cubes. Explain her mistake.

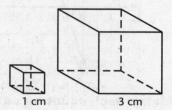

1 cm   3 cm

Find each value.

5. $\dfrac{4(5) + 2^3}{\sqrt{3} + 1}$

6. $\sqrt{\dfrac{7(3) + 3(-4)}{16}}$

Graph each equation. Tell whether the graph is *linear* or *nonlinear*.

7. $y = 3x - 2$

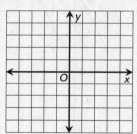

8. $y = x^2 - 1$

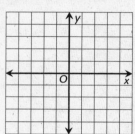

Find the slope of each line.

9.

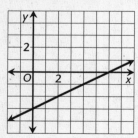

10.

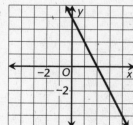

11. The scatter plot shows the change in the population of the United States between 1970 and 2000. The year is on the x-axis and the population, in millions, is on the y-axis.

a. Which equation best fits the line on the scatter plot?

I. $y = 2.7x - 5120$

II. $y = 2.7x$

III. $y = 2.7x + 5120$

b. Use the equation you chose in part (a) to predict the population in the year 2010.

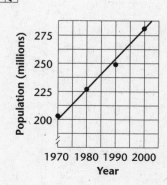

Math Thematics, Book 3
Teacher's Resource Book, Modules 3 and 4

3-30

Solution Guide: Textbook E²

For use with E² on textbook page 191

Mystery State

All of the *Math Thematics Assessment Scales* should be used to assess student work. Students should explain how this puzzle works using a variable for the chosen integer. The student-created puzzle is open-ended and some students may have trouble making their own. Students will need to think of a place, person, or object that can only be chosen with a particular letter. For example, if the letter A is the result of the puzzle and students want to name a state or an animal, there are multiple possibilities (Alabama, Alaska, ant, aardvark, alligator, etc.). Therefore states and animals are not good choices for the letter A.

Some suggestions you can give students are to pick letters that correspond to:

- the first or last initials of U.S. presidents
- types of team sports
- flavors of ice-cream
- kinds of clothing
- styles of music

The sample response below shows part of a student's solution.

Partial Solution

I figured out how this puzzle works by going through the steps using a variable for the number to be chosen.

Directions from the text	**Using a variable and simplifying the expression as I go**
Pick an integer between 1 and 10.	x is the number I choose
Multiply your number by 6.	$6x$
Add 12.	$6x + 12$
Divide by 3.	$\frac{6x + 12}{3} = 2x + 4$
Subtract 4.	$2x + 4 - 4 = 2x$
Divide by your original number.	$\frac{2x}{x} = 2$
Add 4.	$2 + 4 = 6$
Match the number with the corresponding letter of the alphabet (1 = A, 2 = B, etc.).	$6 = F$
Think of a state in the United States that begins with that letter.	The only state in the United States that starts with an F is Florida.
Look at the third letter of the name of the state. Think of a fruit that begins with that letter and grows in that state.	The third letter in Florida is O. The most widely known fruit grown in Florida is oranges.

Since I used a variable, I know this puzzle will work for any number (integers, decimals, and fractions).

Warm-Up Exercises

For use with Section 4

Solve each proportion. Round decimal answers to the nearest tenth.

1. $\dfrac{2}{3} = \dfrac{x}{9}$

2. $\dfrac{20}{16} = \dfrac{5}{x}$

3. $\dfrac{45}{126} = \dfrac{x}{51}$

4. $\dfrac{4.3}{x} = \dfrac{9.7}{21.4}$

5. What are perpendicular lines?

ANSWERS

1. 6   2. 4   3. 18.2   4. 9.5   5. lines that intersect at a right angle

Name _____ Date _____

Two Triangles   (Use with Question 6 on page 194.)

Directions   Use a protractor to construct a triangle, $\triangle DEF$, in which $m\angle D = 50°$ and $m\angle F = 80°$. The lengths of the sides of $\triangle DEF$ should be longer than the sides of $\triangle ABC$.

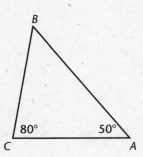

a. Complete the table below. First find the side lengths for $\triangle ABC$ to the nearest tenth of a centimeter. Next name the corresponding sides of $\triangle DEF$, and measure their lengths. Then find the ratio of the lengths of the corresponding sides. Round decimals to the nearest tenth.

$\triangle ABC$	$\triangle DEF$	Ratio of the lengths of the corresponding sides
AB =		
BC =		
AC =		

b. Complete the table below. For $\triangle ABC$, find the measure of $\angle C$. Then name the corresponding angles of $\triangle DEF$ and find their measures.

$\triangle ABC$	$\triangle DEF$
$m\angle A = 50°$	
$m\angle B =$	
$m\angle C = 80°$	

c. In part (b), how did you find the measures of the angles? Describe any "shortcuts" you used.

d. Explain why $\triangle ABC \sim \triangle DEF$.

MODULE 3   **LABSHEET** **4B**

Circle 1 (Use with Question 13 on page 196.)

Directions Follow the directions in your book for cutting and folding the circle.

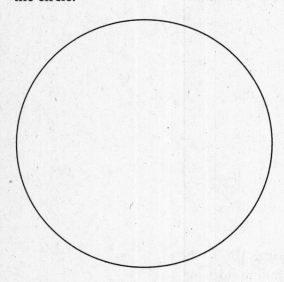

....

Circle 2 (Use with Question 13 on page 196.)

Directions Follow the directions in your book for cutting and folding the circle.

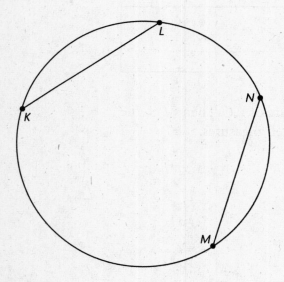

Math Thematics, Book 3
Teacher's Resource Book, Modules 3 and 4

MODULE 3   LABSHEET **4C**

Circular Platter   (Use with Question 17 on page 197.)

Directions The sketch below represents a pottery fragment from a circular platter.

1. **a.** Draw a chord on the pottery fragment.

   b. Open your compass to a radius that is greater than half the length of the chord.

   c. Place the compass point at one endpoint of the chord and draw a circle.

   d. Place the compass point at the other endpoint and draw a circle with the same radius.

   e. Draw a line through the two points where the circles intersect.

2. **a.** Use a protractor to check that the line you drew is perpendicular to the chord.

   b. Use a ruler or a compass to check that the line bisects the chord.

3. Repeat Step 1 with a new chord.

4. Use what you know about perpendicular bisectors of chords to estimate the original diameter of the platter.

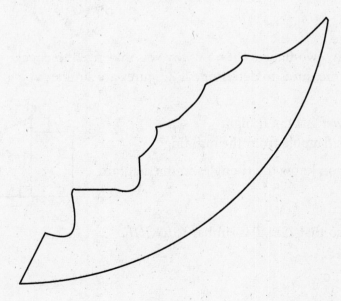

Name _____ Date _____

 3 MODULE

Practice and Applications
For use with Section 4

For use with Exploration 1

For Exercises 1–3, use similar figures *ABCD* and *RSTU*.

1. Find the ratio of the corresponding side lengths.

2. Complete each statement.

   a. $m\angle B = m\angle$ ___?___

   b. $\dfrac{AB}{RS} = \dfrac{BC}{?}$

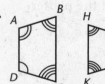

3. Find each measure.

   a. $m\angle R$ **b.** $m\angle D$ **c.** BC

For each pair of figures, write a mathematical statement saying the figures are similar.

4.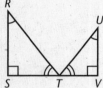

5.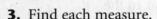

6. **Open-ended** Draw two figures to show why you may need to check more than angle measures to determine if 2 figures are similar. Explain.

7. **a.** The Sears Tower is 1454 ft high. How far is the flagpole from the building?

   b. Explain how you know the triangles in the diagram are similar.

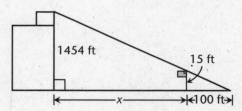

8. Label the angles so that $\triangle EDF$ is similar to $\triangle GHF$.

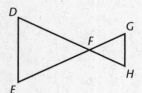

(continued)

Name _____   Date _____

Practice and Applications
For use with Section 4

For use with Exploration 2

9. a. Draw a circle. Then draw two perpendicular diameters. Connect the endpoints to form a rectangle.

  b. What kind of special rectangle did you draw? How could you verify this?

10. a. Draw a circle with a chord perpendicular to a diameter. Connect the endpoints to form a four-sided figure.

  b. Is the figure a parallelogram? Explain.

  c. Label the vertices on the circle in part (a). The diameter divides the figure into two triangles. Measure each angle of both triangles. What do you know about each triangle?

  d. Name one pair of angles in the four-sided figure that are equal.

11. Repeat Exercise 10 using different chords perpendicular to different diameters. Verify that you get the same results.

12. The name for the figure formed in Exercises 10 and 11 is a "kite." Based on your results, name some properties of kites.

13. a. Draw a rectangle. Then draw the two diagonals.

  b. What do you notice about the diagonals? How would you verify this?

  c. Do the diagonals of a rectangle bisect the angles?

  d. Are the triangles that are formed similar?

  e. Draw a rectangle whose diagonals bisect the angles. What kind of rectangle does it appear to be?

14. a. Draw a parallelogram that is not a rectangle. Then draw the diagonals.

  b. What do you notice about the diagonals? How would you verify this?

  c. Do the diagonals of a parallelogram bisect the angles?

  d. Are the triangles similar?

  e. Draw a parallelogram whose diagonals bisect the angles. What kind of parallelogram does it appear to be?

15. a. Draw a circle. Then draw three equal chords that form a triangle.

  b. What kind of triangle is formed?

  c. Draw a circle inside the triangle so that each side of the triangle touches the circle at exactly 1 point. What do you think is true of the two resulting circles?

Study Guide
For use with Section 4

Cliff Dwellers   Similar Figures and Constructions

GOAL   **LEARN HOW TO:** • tell whether triangles are similar
              • make indirect measurements
              • find a perpendicular bisector of a chord

   AS YOU: • estimate the height of a cliff
                • estimate dimensions of artifacts

Exploration 1: Similar Figures

Two figures are **similar** if they have the same shape, but not necessarily
the same size. The symbol ~ means "is similar to." If two figures are
similar, the measures of their **corresponding angles** are equal, and the
ratios of their **corresponding side** lengths are in proportion.

Similar Triangles and Indirect Measurement

Two triangles are similar if two angles of one triangle have the same
measures as two angles of the other triangle. You can use similar triangles
to make indirect measurements and to find missing side lengths.

Example

In the figures at the right, $\triangle ABC$ and $\triangle DEF$
are similar.
a. Find the measures of $\angle D$, $\angle E$, and $\angle F$.
b. Find the lengths of $\overline{DF}$ and $\overline{EF}$.

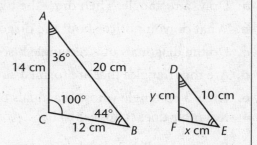

Sample Response

a. Since $\angle D$ corresponds to $\angle A$, then $m\angle D = 36°$.
   Since $\angle E$ corresponds to $\angle B$, then $m\angle E = 44°$.
   Since $\angle F$ corresponds to $\angle C$, then $m\angle F = 100°$.

b. Since $\overline{DE}$ corresponds to $\overline{AB}$, $\overline{EF}$ corresponds to $\overline{BC}$, and $\overline{DF}$ corresponds to $\overline{AC}$, the
   following proportions can be written.

$$\frac{AB}{DE} = \frac{BC}{EF} \qquad \frac{AB}{DE} = \frac{AC}{DF}$$

Inserting the known values gives these proportions:

$$\frac{20}{10} = \frac{12}{x} \qquad \frac{20}{10} = \frac{14}{y}$$

(continued)

Study Guide
For use with Section 4

> ### Sample Response (continued)
>
> The cross products of these proportions form equations that can be solved to find the values of x and y.
>
> $20x = 10(12)$ ← Cross products are equal. → $20y = 10(14)$
> $20x = 120$ ← Divide both sides by 20. → $20y = 140$
> $x = 6$ $y = 7$
>
> So, $EF = 6$ cm and $DF = 7$ cm.

Exploration 2: Bisecting Chords

Circles and Chords

A *circle* is the set of all points in a plane that are a given distance (the *radius*) from a point (the *center* of the circle).

Parts of a Circle

Chord A segment that joins two points on a circle.

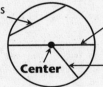

Diameter A chord that passes through the center of a circle.

Radius Any segment that connects a point on the circle to the center.

Center

Perpendicular Bisectors of Two Chords

The **perpendicular bisector** of a chord bisects the chord (divides it into two equal segments), intersecting the chord at a right angle.

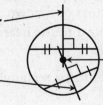

The **perpendicular bisectors** of any two chords on a circle intersect at the center of the circle.

Study Guide: Practice & Application Exercises
For use with Section 4

Exploration 1

For Exercises 1–3, use the similar triangles *ABC* and *EDC*.

1. Find the ratio of the corresponding side lengths.

2. Copy and complete each statement.

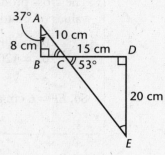

    a. $\dfrac{AB}{ED} = \dfrac{AC}{?}$ **b.** $\dfrac{BC}{?} = \dfrac{?}{EC}$

3. Find each measure.

    a. $m\angle E$ **b.** BC **c.** EC

For each pair of figures, write a mathematical statement saying the figures are similar.

4.
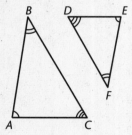

5.
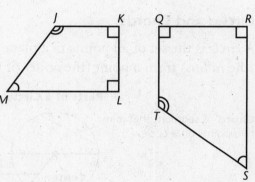

Exploration 2

6. Draw a large circle. Draw and label its center, a diameter, a radius, and two chords. Then draw the perpendicular bisectors of the two chords. Measure and label the two halves of each chord to the nearest centimeter.

7. a. Draw a circle. Then draw four equal chords that form a rectangle.

    b. What kind of special rectangle is formed?

    c. Draw a rectangle inside the special rectangle so that its corners bisect the chords. What do you think is true of the resulting rectangle?

Quick Quiz

For use after Section 4

△ABC ~ △DEF. Use the triangles for Questions 1–3.

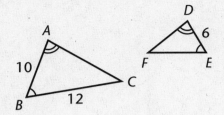

1. Find the ratio of the corresponding side lengths.

2. $m\angle C = m\angle$ _____

3. Find *FE*.

4. A circle with intersecting chords is drawn as shown. Find *AB*.

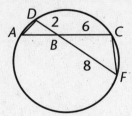

Warm-Up Exercises
For use with Section 5

Find each product.

1. 1.2×10^3

2. 0.8×10^1

3. 345×10^2

Solve each equation.

4. $\dfrac{x}{2} + 7 = 9$

5. $25 = 7x - 10$

ANSWERS

1. 1200   2. 8   3. 34,500   4. 4   5. 5

Name _____   Date _____

Half-Life of Carbon-14   (Use with Question 3 on page 204 and Question 11 on page 207.)

Directions

- Complete the table below.

- Use the data in the table to make a scatter plot on the grid. Draw a smooth curve through the points.

- Describe any patterns you see in the table and graph.

Decay Pattern of Carbon-14			
Number of years	Number of half-lives	Fraction remaining of the original amount of carbon-14	Visual model
0	0	all	
5,730	1	$\frac{1}{2}$	
11,460	2	$\frac{1}{2}$ of $\frac{1}{2} = \frac{1}{2} \cdot \frac{1}{2} = \frac{1}{4}$	
	3	$\frac{1}{2}$ of $\frac{1}{4} =$	

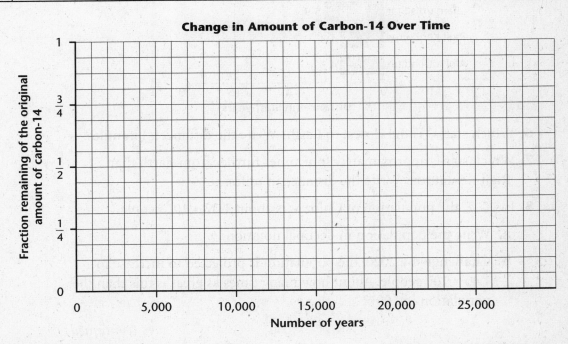

Change in Amount of Carbon-14 Over Time

Math Thematics, Book 3
Teacher's Resource Book, Modules 3 and 4   **3-43**

Name _____ Date _____

Practice and Applications

For use with Section 5

For use with Exploration 1

For Exercises 1–4, write each number in decimal notation.

1. approximate consumption of natural gas in the U.S.:
   $1.86 \cdot 10^{10}$ cubic feet

2. approximate average distance from Jupiter to the sun:
   $7.8 \cdot 10^8$ kilometers

3. approximate time the dinosaurs became extinct: $6.5 \cdot 10^7$ years ago

4. approximate number of atoms in a molecular unit of a substance:
   $6.02 \cdot 10^{23}$

5. Which numbers below are written in scientific notation?

   A. $3.4 \cdot 10^4$ **B.** $62.75 \cdot 10^8$ **C.** $5 \cdot 10^9$

Astronomy Use 1 light-year = 5.88×10^{12} miles and the bar graph below for Exercises 6–8. Note: A light-year is the distance that light travels in a vacuum in one year.

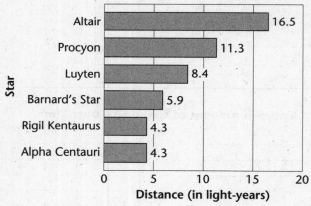

6. Which star(s) is the closest to Earth? Write the distance(s) in miles.

7. Which star is approximately four times further from Earth than Rigil Kentaurus? Write the distance in miles.

8. In 2007, the population of China was about $1.32 \cdot 10^9$ people.

   a. Write the population in decimal notation.

   b. **Challenge** By 2020, the population is projected to increase to $1.45 \cdot 10^9$ people. About how many times as great is this than the population in 2007?

(continued)

Math Thematics, Book 3
3-44 Teacher's Resource Book, Modules 3 and 4

Name _____   Date _____

Practice and Applications

MODULE 3

For use with Section 5

For use with Exploration 2

Solve each equation. Round decimal answers to the nearest hundredth and check your solutions.

9. $22.5 = 1.5x$

10. $0.8y - 3 = 24$

11. $\dfrac{n}{0.4} = 3.2$

12. $8 = 0.5z + 3.5$

13. $6.4 = \dfrac{n}{3.2} - 0.4$

14. $\dfrac{n}{0.05} + 0.75 = 15.5$

15. $-9.5 + 0.75h = -9.5$

16. $0.15s + 13.45 = 13.6$

17. $0.34 - 1.15x = 8.39$

18. $5.5 + 6.5k = -7.5$

19. $-0.5s + 6.5 = 10.8$

20. $1.4x - 0.6 = -25.8$

The number of Calories burned per hour playing tennis is $c = 2.9hw$, where c is the number of Calories, h is the number of hours spent playing tennis, and w is the weight in pounds.

21. a. Jonathan weighs 145 pounds and plays tennis for one hour. How many Calories does he burn?

 b. Estimate the total number of Calories Jonathan burns if he plays tennis for an additional half hour.

 c. Ellen wants to burn 1000 Calories playing tennis. How long would she have to play if she weighs 105 pounds?

The formulas below relate the amount of money Carol and Mary Beth have saved, where w is the number of weeks and a is the amount saved. Each girl saves $4 per week.

Carol
$a = 4w + 105.50$

Mary Beth
$a = 4w + 85.25$

22. Carol saves for 6 weeks. Estimate her savings.

23. Mary Beth saves for 9 weeks. Estimate her savings.

24. Carol wants to save for a bicycle which costs $153.50. How long will it take her to save the money?

25. Will Carol and Mary Beth ever have the same amount saved? Explain.

Name _____ Date _____

Study Guide
For use with Section 5

Forgotten Bones   Scientific Notation and Decimal Equations

GOAL   **LEARN HOW TO:** • write very large numbers in scientific notation
• solve equations involving decimals

AS YOU: • estimate ages of bones
• estimate heights

Exploration 1: Using Scientific Notation

Scientific Notation

In **scientific notation**, a number is written as the product of a decimal
greater than or equal to 1 and less than 10, and a power of 10. You can
change between **decimal notation** and scientific notation.

Example

a. Change the *decimal notation* 42,000 to *scientific notation*.

b. Change the *scientific notation* 5.46 • 10^5 to *decimal notation*.

Sample Response

a. $42,000 = 4.2 \cdot 10,000 = 4.2 \cdot 10^4$

b. $5.46 \cdot 10^5 = 5.46 \cdot 100,000 = 546,000$

Exploration 2: Equations with Decimals

Solving Equations with Decimals

You can use inverse operations to solve an equation with decimals.

Example

Solve $2.4x - 3.5 = 1.9$.

Sample Response

$$2.4x - 3.5 = 1.9$$
$$2.4x - 3.5 + 3.5 = 1.9 + 3.5 \quad \leftarrow \text{Add 3.5 to both sides to undo the subtraction.}$$
$$2.4x = 5.4$$
$$\frac{2.4x}{2.4} = \frac{5.4}{2.4} \quad \leftarrow \text{Divide both sides by 2.4 to undo the multiplication.}$$
$$x = 2.25$$

Name _____ Date _____

Study Guide: Practice & Application Exercises

MODULE 3

For use with Section 5

Exploration 1

Write each number in scientific notation.

1. 4,870,000

2. 300

3. 102,000,000,000

4. 1,200,000,000

5. 890,230,000

6. 16,000,000,000,000

Write each number in decimal notation.

7. $1.9 \cdot 10^4$

8. $3.098 \cdot 10^5$

9. $8 \cdot 10^3$

10. $7.1 \cdot 10^3$

11. $3.52 \cdot 10^8$

12. $1.58 \cdot 10^6$

13. People grow different amounts of hair depending on hair color. The average blonde-haired person can grow about 2.92 million strands of hair in a lifetime. The average red-haired person can grow about 1.72 million strands of hair.

    a. Write each number in scientific notation and in decimal notation.

    b. Compare the number of strands of hair a blonde-haired person and a red-haired person can grow in a lifetime. About how many times as much hair can a blonde-haired person grow as a red-haired person can grow?

Exploration 2

Solve each equation. Round decimal answers to the nearest hundredth and check your solutions.

14. $4.1 = 1.1m - (-1.02)$

15. $\dfrac{y}{6.7} + 10.8 = 2.3$

16. $0.32w + 9.12 = 15.04$

17. $\dfrac{t}{0.04} - 0.13 = 5.12$

18. The formulas below relate the amount of money David and Patrick have earned, where h is the number of hours worked and e is the amount earned. Each boy earns \$5 per hour.

David
$e = 5h + 65.50$

Patrick
$e = 5h + 54.50$

    a. Patrick works for 7 hours. Estimate his earnings to the nearest dollar.

    b. David works for 4 hours. Estimate his earnings to the nearest dollar.

    c. Patrick wants to earn enough money to buy a laptop computer that costs \$450. How many hours will he have to work to earn the money to buy it?

Quick Quiz

For use after Section 5

1. The population of New York declined from 20 million in 1950 to 15.5 million in 1990. Express these numbers in scientific notation.

Solve each equation.

2. $6.5 = 1.3x$

3. $0.25p - 18.5 = 20.25$

4. $\dfrac{n}{0.12} + 3.6 = 2.4$

Math Thematics, Book 3
Teacher's Resource Book, Modules 3 and 4

Warm-Up Exercises

For use with Section 6

Josephine has six pets. Two are frogs, three are turtles, and one is a snake.

1. What percent of the pets are frogs?

2. What percent of the pets are turtles?

3. What percent of the pets are turtles or snakes?

4. What percent of the pets are not snakes?

5. What percent of the pets are not turtles?

ANSWERS

1. $33\frac{1}{3}\%$ 2. 50% 3. $66\frac{2}{3}\%$ 4. $83\frac{1}{3}\%$ 5. 50%

Suspect List (Use with Question 3 on page 215.)

Suspect name	Condensed alibi	Absent from field trip?	Blood type
Alvarado, Winona	On the field trip.	No	O
Blanco, Gloria	Went to the movies.	Yes	A
Chan, Da-wei	Went grocery shopping.	Yes	O
Cooper, LeVerle	At the Crownpoint minimall.	Yes	A
Cordero, Carl	On the field trip.	No	O
Foley, Bridget	At home.	Yes	A
Fuentes, Robert	On the field trip.	No	O
Kelley, Pat	On the field trip.	No	A
Martinez, Perry	At the Crownpoint rodeo.	Yes	A
Mendoza, Luis	On the field trip.	No	O
Nordquist, Karin	On the field trip.	No	AB
Pappas, Sophie	Ran errands in Crownpoint.	Yes	A
Perlman, Morris	On the field trip.	No	A
Puente, Rita	On the field trip.	No	O
Sakiestewa, Willie	Drove to Crownpoint.	Yes	O
Seowtewa, Teresa	At the Crownpoint library.	Yes	A
Stein, Nate	On the field trip.	No	AB
Suarez, Maria Elena	Worked out at a Crownpoint gym.	Yes	A
Sullivan, Michael	Catered a wedding.	Yes	A
Valenzuela, Martina	On the field trip.	No	O
Valenzuela, Pedro	At home.	Yes	O
Weatherwax, Alice	At a conference in Crownpoint.	Yes	A

Math Thematics, Book 3
Teacher's Resource Book, Modules 3 and 4

Name _____   Date _____

 **Practice and Applications**
For use with Section 6

For use with Exploration 1

For Exercises 1–3, tell whether the *or* used is *inclusive* or *exclusive*.

1. Jerome uses his allowance to go to the movies or to buy some popcorn. Jerome has enough money to do both.

2. Juanita wears her hat or her gloves or both.

3. Caroline will read a book or watch television.

For Exercises 4–7, use the Venn diagram at the right.

4. How many students have a morning math class but not a morning science class?

5. How many students have both math and science classes in the morning?

6. What is the total number of students taking math or science classes in the morning?

7. Marya is a new student and is scheduled to take math and science in the morning. Describe how to include her in the Venn diagram.

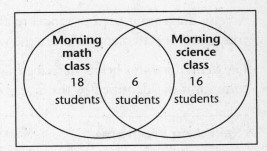

For Exercises 8–9, use the Venn diagram at the right.

8. Which species listed are classified as both threatened and endangered?

9. **Challenge** There are 1192 species that are either endangered, threatened, or both. Estimate what percent is represented by this Venn diagram.

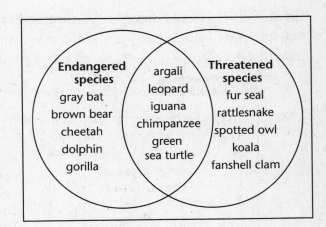

Study Guide
For use with Section 6

Whodunit?   Logical Thinking

GOAL   **LEARN HOW TO:** • interpret statements with *and*, *or*, and *not*
                        • organize information in a Venn diagram
          AS YOU: • analyze clues in a mystery

Exploration 1: Using *And, Or, Not*

Venn Diagram

A **Venn diagram** is used to model relationships among groups. It can help you interpret statements that use the words **and**, **or**, and **not**.

The Venn diagrams below describe the recycling programs of eight communities (identified by the letters A through H).

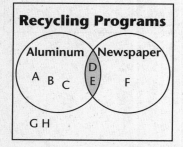

Communities D and E have newspaper *and* aluminum recycling programs.

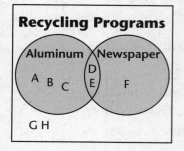

Communities A through F offer newspaper *or* aluminum recycling programs (*or both*).

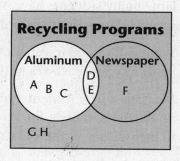

Communities F, G, and H do *not* offer an aluminum recycling program.

Example

Derek Andrew surveyed his class to determine how many of his classmates could speak French and/or Spanish. He made the Venn diagram below.

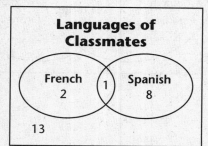

Number of students surveyed: 24
Number of students who speak French but not Spanish: 2
Number of students who speak Spanish but not French: 8
Number of students who speak French *and* Spanish: 1
Number of students that speak French *or* Spanish: 2 + 8 + 1 = 11
Number of students that do *not* speak French and do *not* speak Spanish: 13

Math Thematics, Book 3
Teacher's Resource Book, Modules 3 and 4

Name _____ Date _____

 Study Guide: Practice & Application Exercises
For use with Section 6

Exploration 1

For Exercises 1–5, use the Venn diagram at the right. It shows the results of a survey of students' preferences in flavors of ice cream.

1. Which ice cream flavor was favored by more students, vanilla or chocolate?

2. How many students prefer only chocolate?

3. How many students do not prefer chocolate?

4. How many students prefer both chocolate and vanilla ice cream?

5. How many students were surveyed?

For Exercises 6–8, use the Venn diagram at the right.

6. How many students play tennis or squash?

7. How many students play tennis and squash?

8. How many students do not play tennis and do not play squash?

For Exercises 9–11, use the Venn diagram at the right.

9. Which people have won the ring toss and the egg toss?

10. How many people have won the egg toss?

11. How many people have won the ring toss or the egg toss?

Ice Cream Flavor Preferences

Chocolate 16   10   Vanilla 5

4

Students Who Play Racket Sports

Tennis 13   6   Squash 7

8

State Fair Champions, 2000–2007

Ring Toss		Egg Toss
Ashley Lam	Ty Baker	Barb Evans
Carl McVee	Ron Ito	Vince Kaye
Jamal Jones		Sue Smith

Quick Quiz
For use after Section 6

1. How many speed skaters are listed for the 1000 m event?

2. Which speed skater won both the 500 m and the 1000 m events?

3. How many speed skaters are listed for the 500 m event, the 1000 m event or both?

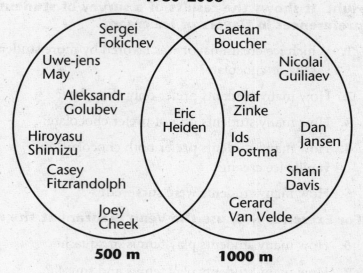

Men's Olympic Speed Skating Gold Medal Winners 1980–2006

Sergei Fokichev
Uwe-jens May
Aleksandr Golubev
Hiroyasu Shimizu
Casey Fitzrandolph
Joey Cheek

Eric Heiden

Gaetan Boucher
Nicolai Guiliaev
Olaf Zinke
Ids Postma
Dan Jansen
Shani Davis
Gerard Van Velde

500 m   **1000 m**

Math Thematics, Book 3
Teacher's Resource Book, Modules 3 and 4

Name _____   Date _____

 Practice and Applications
For use after Sections 1–6

For use with Section 1

Use mental math to find each value.

1. $-\sqrt{121}$ **2.** $\sqrt{0.0009}$ **3.** $\sqrt{\dfrac{1}{49}}$ **4.** $-\sqrt{\dfrac{25}{400}}$

Estimate each square root to the nearest tenth.

5. $-\sqrt{27}$ **6.** $\sqrt{20}$ **7.** $\sqrt{0.4}$ **8.** $-\sqrt{37}$

9. Estimate $\sqrt{75}$ between two consecutive integers.

10. a. Find the side length of a square whose area is 169 m².

  b. Suppose each side of the square in part (a) is multiplied by 3. What is the effect on the area of the square?

For use with Section 2

Evaluate each expression.

11. $\dfrac{7(-5)}{-6+3}$ **12.** $4\sqrt{5-(-20)}$ **13.** $\dfrac{\sqrt{7\cdot 7}}{3}$ **14.** $\dfrac{(-5)^2}{3+2}$

Tell whether each ordered pair is a solution of the equation $y = -2x + 3$.

15. $(3, 4)$ **16.** $(1, 5)$ **17.** $(1, 1)$ **18.** $(3, 3)$

Graph each equation.

19. $y = x + 7$ **20.** $y = -1$ **21.** $y = 8 - 4x$

Graphing Calculator **Graph each equation. Tell whether the graph is *linear* or *nonlinear*.**

22. $y = \dfrac{3}{4}x + 1$ **23.** $y = -2x^2$ **24.** $y = 3x$

For use with Section 3

Plot each pair of points on a coordinate plane and draw a line through them. Find the slope of the line.

25. $(0, 2)$ and $(3, 4)$ **26.** $(-1, -4)$ and $(2, 5)$

27. $(4, 1)$ and $(3, -2)$ **28.** $(2, 2)$ and $(-4, 3)$

(continued)

Name _____   Date _____

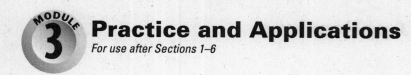

3 Practice and Applications
For use after Sections 1–6

For use with Section 4

29. In the diagram, $\triangle RGT \sim \triangle SGM$. Find the length of $\overline{MG}$.

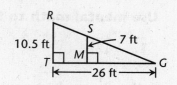

30. In the diagram, $\triangle XYZ \sim \triangle PQR$. Find the length of $\overline{PQ}$.

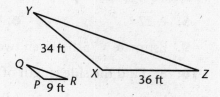

Use a compass to draw a circle with the given radius or diameter.

31. $r = 2.5$ cm   **32.** $d = 4$ cm   **33.** $r = 3$ cm

For use with Section 5

Write each number in scientific notation.

34. 800   **35.** 23,000,000   **36.** 3678

Solve each equation. Round decimal answers to the nearest hundredth and check your solutions.

37. $20 = 1.3x + (-12.5)$ **38.** $\dfrac{f}{2.4} - 32 = -0.9$

39. $5.6 + 0.4g = -1.9$ **40.** $\dfrac{y}{6} + 66.6 = 0.6$

41. $-0.8y + 2.3 = 7.42$ **42.** $48 = -1.9f - (-48.95)$

43. $3.7x + 17 = 30.69$ **44.** $16.93 + 9x = 17.02$

For use with Section 6

Use the Venn diagram for Exercises 45–47.

45. How many students had only toast for breakfast?

46. How many students had both cereal and toast for breakfast?

47. How many students did not have cereal for breakfast?

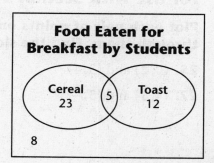

Name _____   Date _____

Suspect List (Use with Project Question 15 on page 224.)

Suspect name	Condensed alibi	Absent from field trip?	Blood type	Height (cm)
Alvarado, Winona	On the field trip.	No	O	168
Blanco, Gloria	Went to the movies.	Yes	A	160
Chan, Da-wei	Went grocery shopping.	Yes	O	175
Cooper, LeVerle	At the Crownpoint minimall.	Yes	A	182
Cordero, Carl	On the field trip.	No	O	185
Foley, Bridget	At home.	Yes	A	188
Fuentes, Robert	On the field trip.	No	O	187
Kelley, Pat	On the field trip.	No	A	158
Martinez, Perry	At the Crownpoint rodeo.	Yes	A	
Mendoza, Luis	On the field trip.	No	O	175
Nordquist, Karin	On the field trip.	No	AB	170
Pappas, Sophie	Ran errands in Crownpoint.	Yes	A	190
Perlman, Morris	On the field trip.	No	A	182
Puente, Rita	On the field trip.	No	O	174
Sakiestewa, Willie	Drove to Crownpoint.	Yes	O	180
Seowtewa, Teresa	At the Crownpoint library.	Yes	A	175
Stein, Nate	On the field trip.	No	AB	190
Suarez, Maria Elena	Worked out at a Crownpoint gym.	Yes	A	160
Sullivan, Michael	Catered a wedding.	Yes	A	182
Valenzuela, Martina	On the field trip.	No	O	170
Valenzuela, Pedro	At home.	Yes	O	173
Weatherwax, Alice	At a conference in Crownpoint.	Yes	A	

Drawing Conclusions (Use with Project Question 17 on page 225.)

Directions

- Use the map and scale to estimate distances from nearby towns to the Blacktail Canyon research site.

- Compare your estimated distances with the suspects' alibis to determine whether the thief could have traveled the distance to the research site.

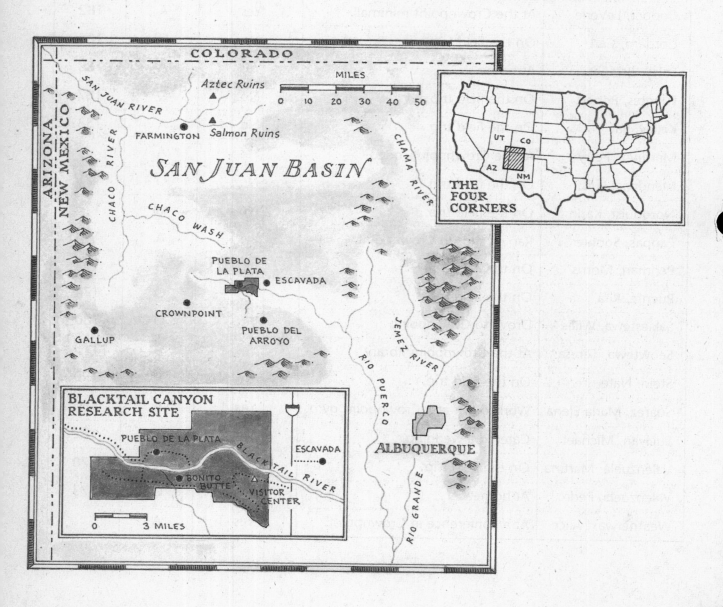

MODULE 3 **CLUE CARDS for THE MODULE PROJECT**

Clues Handout Set #1

LeVerle Cooper and Teresa Seowtewa have access to the closet.	Michael Sullivan just moved to Escavada.	LeVerle Cooper knows the area well, but Maria Elena Suarez does not.	Sophie Pappas and Perry Martinez both grew up in Escavada.
Red hairs from a wig were found in a comb in the backpack found in the school closet.	LeVerle Cooper does not have a cut on his head, but Maria Elena Suarez does.	Sophie Pappas has a cut on her head.	Alice Weatherwax has a key to the school closet.
Alice Weatherwax has lived in Escavada for 9 years.	Perry Martinez has keys to the school closet, but Sophie Pappas does not.	Teresa Seowtewa does not know the area well.	It did not rain in Crownpoint on the day of the theft.
Teresa Seowtewa always wears a hat.	Gloria Blanco was not at the movies.	Perry Martinez and the librarian at Crownpoint are good friends.	The door to the closet was found locked. It showed no signs of having been forced open.
The thief used the school closet to hide some of the pottery pieces.	There is a cut on the thief's head.	The thief knows the area well.	Perry Martinez likes to rock climb.

MODULE 3   CLUE CARDS for THE MODULE PROJECT

Clues Handout Set #2

Michael Sullivan and Alice Weatherwax have access to the closet.	Maria Elena Suarez just moved to Escavada.	Michael Sullivan knows the area well, but Alice Weatherwax does not.	LeVerle Cooper grew up in Escavada, but Maria Elena Suarez did not.
Red hairs from a wig were found in a comb in the backpack found in the school closet.	Alice Weatherwax and Teresa Seowtewa each has a cut on her head.	Sophie Pappas has a cut on her head, but LeVerle Cooper and Michael Sullivan do not.	Perry Martinez and Teresa Seowtewa have keys to the school closet.
Teresa Seowtewa has lived in Escavada for 12 years.	LeVerle Cooper has keys to the school closet, but Sophie Pappas does not.	Perry Martinez knows the area well.	It did not rain in Crownpoint on the day of the theft.
Maria Elena Suarez always wears a hat.	Gloria Blanco was not at the movies.	Sophie Pappas and the librarian at Crownpoint are good friends.	The door to the closet was found locked. It showed no signs of having been forced open.
The thief used the school closet to hide some of the pottery pieces.	There is a cut on the thief's head.	The thief knows the area well.	Michael Sullivan likes to rock climb.

MODULE 3		CLUE CARDS for THE MODULE PROJECT	

Clues Handout Set #3

Michael Sullivan has access to the closet.	Michael Sullivan just moved to Escavada.	Alice Weatherwax knows the area well, but Perry Martinez does not.	LeVerle Cooper and Teresa Seowtewa grew up in Escavada.
Red hairs from a wig were found in a comb in the back-pack found in the school closet.	LeVerle Cooper does not have a cut on his head, but Teresa Seowtewa does.	Perry Martinez has a cut on his head.	Alice Weatherwax and Teresa Seowtewa have keys to the school closet.
Gloria Blanco was not at the movies.	Maria Elena Suarez has keys to the school closet, but Sophie Pappas does not.	Maria Elena Suarez does not know the area well.	It did not rain in Crownpoint on the day of the theft.
LeVerle Cooper always wears a hat.	Sophie Pappas often visits the Crownpoint library.	Maria Elena Suarez and the librarian at Crownpoint are good friends.	The door to the closet was found locked. It showed no signs of having been forced open.
The thief used the school closet to hide some of the pottery pieces.	There is a cut on the thief's head.	The thief knows the area well.	LeVerle Cooper likes to rock climb.

MODULE 3	TRANSCRIPTS for THE MODULE PROJECT

FILE: Cooper, LeVerle

OCCUPATION: Science Teacher

FILE NUMBER: 123-1

INTERVIEWER: Sgt. Jack Sanchez (JS)

Transcript excerpt—L. Cooper (LC)

JS: Mr. Cooper, you attended Dr. Ashilaka's lecture last week. Are you interested in archaeology?

LC: Yes, I am. Very interested! I'm planning to do a little exploring myself. To, you know, to find a new site and, well, make a little money. Through publishing, and lecturing, and such.

JS: So you must've enjoyed Dr. Ashilaka's field trip?

LC: Yes. No! No, I didn't go. I had to run into Crownpoint to do a little shopping.

JS: Did you see anyone you knew while you were there?

LC: (angry) No! I didn't see anyone! I just went shopping and ate lunch! I was at the mini-mall at 11 o'clock and I ate lunch at 12. Ate lunch alone! Alone at the park!

JS: And then where did you go?

LC: Nowhere. For a lonely walk in the desert. At about 4 o'clock, I went back to shopping.

Transcript excerpt—K. C. Crews (KC), Sales-clerk, Crownpoint Men's Store

JS: Mr. Crews, this is a photo of a man we're interested in. Have you ever seen him before? [Note: photo of LeVerle Cooper]

KC: He was in my store last week! He sure looked guilty! Handling the goods, but always looking over his shoulder. I spotted him right away. He left and later came back.

JS: What time was that, Mr. Crews? When he left, and when he got back.

KC: Let's see, he was there about an hour, so I guess he left about noon. Check with Devon, the manager. She said she saw him outside at lunch. He was back as I was leaving. My shift ends at 4, so it must've been about 4:15. So what'd he do? Murder?

Transcript excerpt—Devon Dupuis (DD), Manager, Crownpoint Men's Store

JS: Do you recognize this man, Ms. Dupuis? [Note: photo of LeVerle Cooper]

DD: Oh, the man Mr. Crews thought looked suspicious! Yes, I recognize him. He didn't actually steal anything, though.

JS: Ms. Dupuis, did you see this man after he left your store?

DD: I did! He was having a picnic in the park with an attractive woman. They looked romantic. That was during my lunch break, between 12 and 12:30. Did he do whatever it was?

JS: Hard to say, ma'am.

Name _____   Date _____

| MODULE 3 | TRANSCRIPTS for THE MODULE PROJECT |

FILE: Martinez, Perry   **FILE NUMBER:** 222-2

OCCUPATION: Mathematics Teacher   **INTERVIEWER:** Sgt. Jack Sanchez (JS)

Transcript excerpt—P. Martinez (PM)

PM: Anasazi-schmazi! I couldn't care less about all those old dead people and their broken pots and pans. I was there to kill time before the Math Club showed up. We were off to the Crownpoint Rodeo to sell fry bread and Indian tacos. It's a fundraiser for the Club.

JS: So you didn't stay 'til the end of the lecture?

PM: Well, I did. The kids were due to show up after the doc finished and he spun a good yarn.

JS: So I guess you sat with the kids at the stand all day.

PM: Well, no. Listen, don't tell any of the parents, but I just check 'em in, set 'em up, and let 'em go to work. I hate all that macho cowboy stuff. Give me a rope and a rock to climb, and I'm happy. I stay in Vendor's Alley in case they need me, but they never do.

JS: And can anyone verify that you stayed in Vendor's Alley the whole time?

PM: Phil Tewa, a Crownpoint guy, checked me in. But the place is always crowded, so a lot of people saw me, but maybe nobody noticed me. Somebody bumped me from behind during the rain, and I fell and cracked my head. I sat there bleeding, and nobody even noticed! Hey, are you trying to make it sound like I snuck away or something?

JS: No sir. Just trying to get the facts.

PM: (angry) Well, the fact is, no one leaves or enters the Alley without checking out or checking in! Ask Tewa! He'll tell you! I checked in once, and checked out once! Besides, I wouldn't take a load of kids to a rodeo and just leave them there. They'd eat all the profits!

Transcript excerpt—Phil Tewa (PT), Crownpoint Rodeo Vendor Official

PT: Yeah, I remember the Math Club. They come every year. Mr. Martinez signs the papers and then lets the kids do all the work.

JS: You also handle the first aid, don't you? Did Martinez come to you with his head injury after the rain?

PT: What rain? The sun baked us all day! But I did notice that cut on his head when the club checked out. I told him to go to the ER for stitches.

JS: You've been very helpful, Mr. Tewa. Oh, maybe you can help us track down a stranger who was in Crownpoint on the day of the rodeo. He, or she, has red hair.

PT: Oh, that clown! Yeah, I saw him. I gave him a pass to leave the Alley just after we opened at 11 o'clock. He must've been helping someone set up and clean up, because he didn't come back until after 4 some time. I never did figure out who he was working for.

MODULE 3   TRANSCRIPTS for THE MODULE PROJECT

FILE: Martinez, Perry   **FILE NUMBER:** 113-2

OCCUPATION: Mathematics Teacher   **INTERVIEWER:** Sgt. Jack Sanchez (JS)

....

Transcript excerpt—P. Martinez (PM)

PM: Anasazi-schmazi! I couldn't care less about all those old dead people and their broken pots and pans. I was there to kill time before the Math Club showed up. We were off to the Crownpoint Rodeo to sell fry bread and Indian tacos. It's a fundraiser for the Club.

JS: So you didn't stay 'til the end of the lecture?

PM: Well, I did. The kids were due to show up after the doc finished and he spun a good yarn.

JS: So I guess you sat with the kids at the stand all day.

PM: Well, no. Listen, don't tell any of the parents, but I just check 'em in, set 'em up, and let 'em go to work. I hate all that macho cowboy stuff. Give me a rope and a rock to climb, and I'm happy. I stay in Vendor's Alley in case they need me, but they never do.

JS: And can anyone verify that you stayed in Vendor's Alley the whole time?

PM: Phil Tewa, a Crownpoint guy, checked me in. But the place is always crowded, so a lot of people saw me, but maybe nobody noticed me. Somebody bumped me from behind, and I fell and cracked my head. I sat there bleeding, and nobody even noticed. Hey, are you trying to make it sound like I snuck away or something?

JS: No sir. Just trying to get the facts.

PM: (angry) Well, the fact is, no one leaves or enters the Alley without checking out or checking in! Ask Tewa! He'll tell you! I checked in once, and checked out once! Besides, I wouldn't take a load of kids to a rodeo and just leave them there. They'd eat all the profits!

Transcript excerpt—Phil Tewa (PT), Crownpoint Rodeo Vendor Official

PT: Yeah, I remember the Math Club. They come every year. Mr. Martinez signs the papers and then lets the kids do all the work.

JS: You also handle the first aid, don't you? Did Martinez come to you with his head injury?

PT: Oh, yeah! We see a lot of cuts and scrapes. I put a couple of butterfly bandages on his forehead and told him to go to the ER for stitches when he left. That was right about lunchtime.

JS: You've been very helpful, Mr. Tewa. Oh, maybe you can help us track down a stranger who was in Crownpoint on the day of the rodeo. He, or she, has red hair.

PT: Oh, that clown! He tried to sneak into the Alley, but I snagged him. The cops took him downtown and held him the rest of the day.

Math Thematics, Book 3
Teacher's Resource Book, Modules 3 and 4

Name _____   Date _____

FILE: Pappas, Sophia   **FILE NUMBER:** 123-3

OCCUPATION: Owner/Operator   **INTERVIEWER:** Sgt. Jack Sanchez (JS)
             Escavada Biking Adventures

Transcript excerpt—S. Pappas (SP)

SP: My gosh, yes, I was at Dr. Ashilaka's lecture last week. I make it my business to learn everything I can about the area's trivia. It was great stuff, but I disagree with his theory. He thinks the Anasazi lived in caves for defense. But I think they were peaceful farmers who found rocks were a natural air conditioner.

JS: Yes, ma'am. And then where did you go after the lecture?

SP: Oh, I cruised into Crownpoint to run errands. I was at the town's combination rock climbing/rollerblading store at about 11 o'clock. I picked up some new chains and cranks. I talked with Scotty Dog Daniels for a while, and then had an iced cappuccino with him. Then I ran to the local natural foods store for a case of granola bars and a couple pounds of dried fruit. Fergy Ferguson helped me there. She'll remember every detail. After that I took a bike ride up Owl Creek trail and darn near killed myself!

JS: How's that, ma'am?

SP: You see, I always wear my helmet when I ride, but take it off as soon as I stop. I climbed up on one boulder, and jumped to the next without looking. There was an overhanging ledge that caught me right in the head. It almost killed me. When I got down from Owl Creek, I went straight back to the rock climbing store for some sympathy. I didn't get any from Scotty Dog, so I came home.

JS: At what time, ma'am?

SP: Time? I was happy to be alive! I didn't bother to check my watch.

Transcript excerpt—Scot "Scotty Dog" Daniels (SD), Owner, Climbing and 'Blading

JS: Mr. Daniels, do you recall the last time Sophia Pappas visited your shop?

SD: Oh, Soapy? Yeah, she came by last week, I think. Just before I opened. About 11 or 12. We shared a pop or something. Yeah, well it was something cold. She came back just as I was closing. She had a headache or something.

JS: And when is closing, Mr. Daniels?

SD: When? Oh! You mean closing! Uh, do you mean, when did she come back?

Transcript excerpt—Rebecca "Fergy" Ferguson (RF), Clerk at the Food Co-Op

RF: Sophie stopped by at 11:50. She bought a case of granola bars, and a pound each of dried apples, banana chips, and trail mix, all with a member's 5% discount. She paid with a check and left by the back door at 12:15. Anything else you need to know?

JS: (pause) Uh… no ma'am. Thank you, ma'am.

Name _____   Date _____

FILE: Seowtewa, Teresa   FILE NUMBER: 333-4

OCCUPATION: Social Studies Teacher   INTERVIEWER: Sgt. Jack Sanchez (JS)

....

Transcript excerpt—T. Seowtewa (TS)

JS: So what brought you to Dr. Ashilaka's lecture? Are you an archaeologist?

TS: Yes, in a way. I'm a social studies teacher, and I have a great unit on the Anasazi. Ashilaka's lecture was a great chance to get some recent information. He's the best there is! I stayed for the whole thing! I just wish he could've talked longer! But I had to rush over to the Crownpoint Library. I had made arrangements to get in to do some research.

JS: Can anyone verify that you were actually at the library?

TS: (angry) Yes, of course! Linda Balboa, the archivist, keeps the key. She let me in! It must've been quarter to eleven or so. Does that matter?

JS: It's hard to say, ma'am. Did you leave the building at any time?

TS: No. I tried to leave for lunch, but I hadn't expected the rain. I just skipped lunch and worked straight through until 4 o'clock. I wanted to get back to Escavada by five.

JS: Can anyone confirm that?

TS: That's your job, isn't it? You can check with Linda. She had to lock up when I left.

Transcript excerpt—L. Balboa (LB), Crownpoint Librarian

LB: Sure I remember that day. It must've been a little before 11 o'clock when Teresa arrived. She made a big fuss about all the work she had, and how she wasn't to be disturbed.

JS: Was she in the library all day?

LB: I guess so. I slipped out at noon to eat lunch on the bench and enjoy the sun. It was a beautiful day. Anyway, I got the key back from Teresa at about 4 o'clock. I leave her the key so she can come and go without bothering me to lock up.

JS: Did you notice anything odd about her behavior?

LB: No, she was the same as always. Except for the gash. Oh, the poor thing! She pulled one of those big pieces of pottery from Chaco Canyon right down on her head. It must have happened while I was out to lunch, because I didn't hear anything. But I saw the bump! It gave her a nasty cut!

JS: Thank you, Ms. Balboa. You've been very helpful. Oh, and before I go, I was just wondering if you saw any strangers in town that day. Especially red heads.

LB: Isn't that funny. There was a person just like that. I saw her, dressed in a raincoat and sunglasses, leaving as I went to lunch. I noticed her coming back in about 3 o'clock. I wonder where she went from there?

Name _____   Date _____

FILE: Seowtewa, Teresa   **FILE NUMBER:** 112-4

OCCUPATION: Social Studies Teacher   **INTERVIEWER:** Sgt. Jack Sanchez (JS)

....

Transcript excerpt—T. Seowtewa (TS)

JS: So what brought you to Dr. Ashilaka's lecture? Are you an archaeologist?

TS: Yes, in a way. I'm a social studies teacher, and I have a great unit on the Anasazi. Ashilaka's lecture was a great chance to get some recent information. He's the best there is! I stayed for the whole thing! I just wish he could've talked longer! But I had to rush over to the Crownpoint Library. I had made arrangements to get in to do some research.

JS: Can anyone verify that you were actually at the library?

TS: (angry) Yes, of course! Linda Balboa, the archivist, keeps the key. She let me in! It must've been quarter to eleven or so. Does that matter?

JS: It's hard to say, ma'am. Did you leave the building at any time?

TS: No. I skipped lunch and worked until 4 o'clock. I wanted to get back to Escavada by five.

JS: Can anyone confirm that?

TS: That's your job, isn't it? You can check with Linda. She had to lock up when I left.

Transcript excerpt—L. Balboa (LB), Crownpoint Librarian

LB: Sure I remember that day. It must've been a little before 11 o'clock when Teresa arrived. She made a big fuss about all the work she had, and how she wasn't to be disturbed.

JS: Was she in the library all day?

LB: I guess so. I saw her at about noon. It was a beautiful day so I asked her to join me for lunch outside to enjoy the sun. But she was too busy. Anyway, I locked up as Teresa was leaving at about 4 o'clock.

JS: Did you notice anything odd about her behavior?

LB: No, she was the same as always. Except for the gash. Oh, the poor thing! She pulled one of those big pieces of pottery right down on her head. We keep a few examples of the main types of pots from Chaco Canyon for the researchers to refer to. It gave her a nasty cut!

JS: Did you see the accident?

LB: Well, no… She was alone at the time. But I heard the crash and then saw the bump!

JS: Thank you, Ms. Balboa. You've been very helpful. Oh, and before you go, I was just wondering if you've seen any suspicious people in town. Especially red heads.

LB: Red heads? Only some of those school kids. But then that's not really red, is it? It's usually pink, or green, or purple… or sometimes all three.

Name _____ Date _____

FILE: Suarez, Maria Elena   **FILE NUMBER:** 123-5

OCCUPATION: Health & Fitness Teacher   **INTERVIEWER:** Sgt. Jack Sanchez (JS)

....

Transcript excerpt—M.E. Suarez (MES)

JS: Just a few questions concerning your activities on the day of the Blacktail Canyon theft, Ms. Suarez. It won't take long. Uh… Do you have to do push-ups right now?

MES: 12, 13—You're cutting into my work-out,—17, 18, 19—so, if you don't mind—23, 24—I'll keep at it while you play Sherlock Holmes—30! You look like you could use a little more activity yourself! Stop by sometime and I'll design a fitness program for you.

JS: Right… Now, can you tell me why you attended Dr. Ashilaka's lecture?

MES: I'm new in the area. I do a lot of sight-seeing while biking, or jogging, or climbing. (Do you mind if I put my feet on your table?) I was just trying to get a little back-ground on the land. Say, did you notice Ashilaka's triceps? Great definition!

JS: And where did you go after the lecture?

MES: Let's see. That was a weight training day—so I ran into the Crownpoint Fitness Center.

JS: Can anyone confirm your activities there?

MES: It was a slow day. Consuela Estrada was there when I arrived, but she left for a three-hour run. I had the place to myself until about 2 o'clock. I might have bled to death on that floor. I was pumping free-weights, and got in a groove. You know, when your body's like iron and it just won't quit. Maybe you don't know. Anyway, I was working opposite biceps with 20 pound dumbbells, and just whacked myself up-side the head! I was decked!

JS: Did you see a doctor?

MES: Doctor? My body's strong enough to heal itself! Once we got the bleeding stopped, I took a ten-mile bike ride to get my rhythm back. I played in the volleyball tournament that night.

Transcript excerpt—Consuela Estrada (CE), Fitness Center Employee

CE: You mean the day Maria Suarez nearly iced herself? Yeah, I remember. I started my run at about 11 o'clock, so I guess she pulled in at about quarter 'til.

JS: And then you found her when you returned?

CE: Cold as a mackerel in a pool of blood. I thought she'd, you know, cashed it in! Bought the farm! Died! I patched her back together and loaded her on her bike and she took off. That was just after two. I haven't seen her since. She didn't die after all, did she?

JS: No, no. She still seems reasonably healthy.

CE: Ya know, Slim, it wouldn't hurt you to see the inside of a gym once in a while, either.

JS: Thanks for your help, Ms. Estrada. I've got to go. I hear a jelly Danish calling my name.

MODULE 3   **TRANSCRIPTS for THE MODULE PROJECT**

FILE: Sullivan, Michael   **FILE NUMBER:** 123-6

OCCUPATION: Escavada School Food   **INTERVIEWER:** Sgt. Jack Sanchez (JS)
Service/Michael's
Catering Service

....

Transcript excerpt—M. Sullivan (MS)

JS: So you attended Dr. Ashilaka's lecture last week. Is that right?

MS: Right. Great stuff! I love all that ancient mystery stuff. I stayed until it ended. Must've been about 10 o'clock. I had a job in Crownpoint. During the year I work in the school cafeteria, but in the summer I run Michael's Catering.

JS: So you worked in Crownpoint all day?

MS: I was supposed to. I just did one thing wrong. I left my crêpe pan in Escavada. There's a hardware store in Crownpoint, but would Michelangelo buy his chisels from a hardware store? This is a pan forged in Denmark and hand seasoned by Chef Pierre Monet in France!

JS: Uh huh... So you're saying you had to run back to Escavada to get this... crêpe pan?

MS: Yes. I had just put in the corn bread. It must've been about 11:30. I had just enough time to get to Escavada and back. But when I was almost to town, the rain made visibility so bad, I had to slow down to 20. It rained like that for a half hour. By the time I got back to Crownpoint, the fire department had just put out my corn bread. There was so much smoke, I'm not sure who fired me, but I think it was Mrs. vanderWettering.

JS: Can someone verify those times?

MS: Sure! At least fifty guests at the vanderWettering wedding.

Transcript excerpt—Eloise vanderWettering (EV)

JS: Yes, ma'am. This will only take a minute. We're trying to verify the activities of Michael Sullivan on the day of your daughter's wedding last week.

EV: Michael Sullivan? Never heard of him!

JS: He runs Michael's Catering Service.

EV: Him?! That monster?! That imbecile?! That... that... destroyer of families?!! Can I verify his activities? He was actively ruining my daughter's wedding!

JS: Uh, yes, well, thank you, ma'am. And at what time was that?

EV: I'll tell you what time!! It was the last time my daughter spoke to me! The photo session began at 12:30. The smoke alarms and sprinkler system went off at about 12:40. The volunteers of the Crownpoint Fire Department were there by 12:45, and Michael made his entrance shortly after that, say 12:50. I hope you find that helpful, officer. Now, if you'll just show me where this Michael creature is, I'll put him out of his misery.

MODULE 3	TRANSCRIPTS for THE MODULE PROJECT

FILE: Weatherwax, Alice   **FILE NUMBER:** 223-7

OCCUPATION: Escavada School Principal   **INTERVIEWER:** Sgt. Jack Sanchez (JS)

....

Transcript excerpt—A. Weatherwax (AW)

JS: Just a few questions, Ms. Weatherwax. We have to interview all the suspects.

AW: Make it a very few. I have more important things to do than to sit here and be bothered.

JS: Yes, ma'am. Why did you attend Dr. Ashilaka's lecture? Do you collect Anasazi pottery?

AW: Good heavens, no! Nothing but a bunch of dusty dishes. No, I collect contemporary southwestern art. But many of the artists are influenced by Anasazi pottery designs.

JS: What time did you leave the lecture?

AW: Just as soon as he stopped rambling. Most boring man I've ever heard! From there I went straight to Crownpoint for the Association of School Administrators conference. The opening address was at 11 o'clock. The conference lasted all day. I was exhausted!

JS: Yes, ma'am. Did anyone actually see you there? Did you sit with a friend?

AW: I don't have many friends. But I was at the opening, and then at Dobson's lecture, and then… Well, I did present a 5 o'clock lecture myself. You might ask any of the fifty people who attended that. Or ask Dave Fiorillo. He was at the registration desk.

Transcript excerpt—Dave Fiorillo (DF), conference registration

JS: So you handled the registration of all 5,000 participants at the conference?

DF: I sat at the table all day. I stamped their hands if they left, so they could get back in. It was chaos when Ashley's lecture was canceled. Everyone wanted to leave to enjoy the sunshine.

JS: Do you recall if Alice Weatherwax was there?

DF: Ol' Battle-ax Weatherwax? Sure. She's not the sort of person to slip by unnoticed. Yeah, she was punctual as usual. Just in time for the Opening Address.

JS: Did she leave at any time during the day?

DF: Oh, no. She would have to get her hand stamped, and I would have noticed. Besides, she lectured at 5 o'clock. Best lecture she ever gave! It was that bump and dried blood on her head! The room was packed with people waiting to see if she would pass out! The rumor is a projection screen fell on her head. It should have been something heavier.

JS: One more thing. Did you notice any suspicious persons with red hair at the conference?

DF: A few ridiculous ones with hair dyed red, but there are some of those every year.

| MODULE 3 | TRANSCRIPTS for THE MODULE PROJECT |

FILE: Weatherwax, Alice   **FILE NUMBER:** 111-7

OCCUPATION: Escavada School Principal   **INTERVIEWER:** Sgt. Jack Sanchez (JS)

....

Transcript excerpt—A. Weatherwax (AW)

JS: Just a few questions, Ms. Weatherwax. We have to interview all the suspects.

AW: Make it a very few. I have more important things to do than to sit here and be bothered.

JS: Yes, ma'am. Why were you at Dr. Ashilaka's lecture? Do you collect Anasazi pottery?

AW: Good heavens, no! Nothing but a bunch of dusty dishes. No, I collect contemporary southwestern art. But many of the artists are heavily influenced by Anasazi designs.

JS: What time did you leave the lecture?

AW: Just as soon as he stopped rambling. Most boring man I've ever heard! From there I went straight to Crownpoint for the Association of School Administrators conference. The opening address was at 11 o'clock. The conference lasted all day. I was exhausted!

JS: Yes, ma'am. Did anyone actually see you there? Did you sit with a friend?

AW: I don't have many friends. But I was at the opening, and then at Ashley's lecture during the rain, and then... Well, I did present a 5 o'clock lecture myself. You might ask any of the fifty people who attended. Or ask Dave Fiorillo. He was at the registration desk.

Transcript excerpt—Dave Fiorillo (DF), conference registration

JS: So you handled the registration of all 5,000 participants at the conference?

DF: I sat at the table all day. I stamped their hands if they left, so they could get back in. It was chaos when Ashley's lecture was canceled. Everyone wanted to leave to enjoy the sunshine.

JS: Do you recall if Alice Weatherwax was there?

DF: Ol' Battle-ax Weatherwax? Sure. She's not the sort of person to slip by unnoticed. Yeah, she was punctual as usual. Just in time for the Opening Address.

JS: Did she leave at any time during the day?

DF: Oh, no. She would have to get her hand stamped, and I would have noticed. Besides, she lectured at 5 o'clock. Best lecture she ever gave! It was that bump and dried blood on her head! The room was packed with people waiting to see if she would pass out! The rumor is a projection screen fell on her head. It should have been something heavier.

JS: One more thing. Did you notice any suspicious persons with red hair at the conference?

DF: Hey, there was somebody! An eccentric woman in a raincoat and sunglasses. She left during the Opening Address, and didn't get back until after 4. I know because I stamped her hand to check her back in. Funny. No one could remember when she actually registered.

MODULE 3   **REVIEW AND ASSESSMENT LABSHEET**

Diameter of a Tree Trunk (Use with Exercise 18 on page 227.)

Directions

• Use paperfolding and the outer tree trunk section shown below to determine the approximate length of the diameter of the tree trunk.

• Mark a radius and a chord.

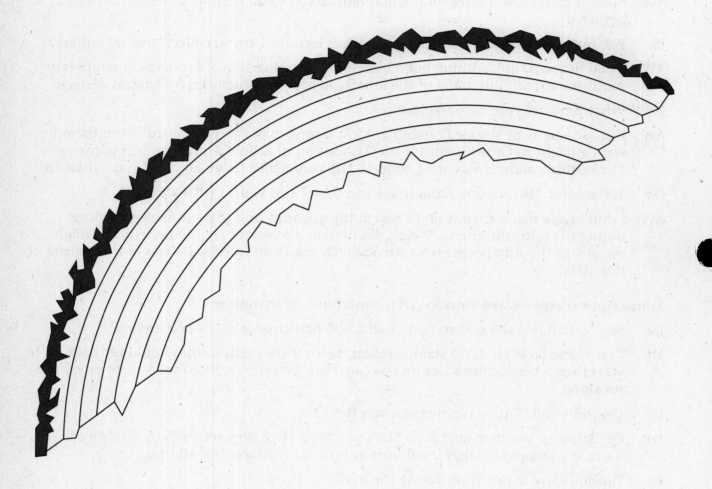

Math Thematics, Book 3
Teacher's Resource Book, Modules 3 and 4

Test Form A
For use after Module 3

Find each value. Describe your method. Tell whether your answer is exact or an estimate.

1. $\sqrt{0.36}$

2. $\sqrt{10,000}$

3. $\sqrt{84}$

4. Amy estimated that the larger box will hold just two of the smaller boxes. Explain her mistake.

Evaluate each expression.

5. $\dfrac{6 \cdot 3^2 + 30}{\sqrt{7} + 2}$

6. $\sqrt{\dfrac{6(7) + 3(-2)}{25}}$

Graph each equation. Tell whether the graph is *linear* or *nonlinear*.

7. $y = -3x + 1$

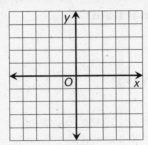

8. $y = x^2 + 2$

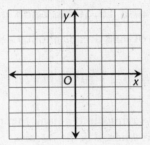

Find the slope of each line.

9.

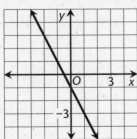

10.

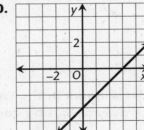

11. Find the height of the building if the tree shown is 10 ft tall.

Test Form A
For use after Module 3

12. The scatter plot shows the number of subscribers for a cable
television service between 1990 and 1994. The year is on the x-axis
and the number of subscribers is on the y-axis (in thousands).

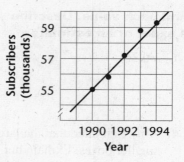

a. Which equation best fits the line on the scatter plot?

    I. $y = 1.08x + 2094$
   II. $y = 1.08x$
  III. $y = 1.08x - 2094$

b. Use the equation you chose in part (a) to predict the number of
subscribers in the year 2000.

Write each number in scientific notation.

13. In 2005, there were about 75,780,000 students enrolled in public school in
the United States.

14. In 2007, there were about 6,602,000,000 people in the world.

For Questions 15 and 16, write each number in decimal notation.

15. The world total of land area is about $1.48 \cdot 10^8$ km^2.

16. Consumers spent $4.22 \cdot 10^{10}$ dollars on books and maps in 2005.

17. Sophia puts her savings into a bank that pays interest according to the following
formula: $I = Prt$, where I is the interest, P is the principal (the amount she saves),
r is the rate, and t is the length of time in years. If she saves $150.50, explain
how to find the amount of money she will have at the end of one year if she is
paid a rate of 5%.

**The table shows the gold medal winners in the Women's Olympic
500 m and 1000 m Short Track Speed Skating competitions from
1992 to 2006.**

18. Make a Venn diagram that includes the skaters listed.

19. Which skater(s) won a gold medal in both the 500 m and
1000 m races?

20. How many skaters won a gold medal in either the 500 m or
1000 m race?

500 m	1000 m
Cathy Turner	Lee-Kyung Chun
Annie Perreault	Yang Yang (A)
Yang Yang (A)	Sun-Yu Jin
Meng Wang	

Name _____ Date _____

Test Form B
For use after Module 3

Find each value. Describe your method. Tell whether your answer is exact or an estimate.

1. $\sqrt{0.01}$

2. $-\sqrt{900}$

3. $\sqrt{63}$

4. Russ estimated that the larger box will hold the same amount as just two of the smaller boxes. Explain his mistake.

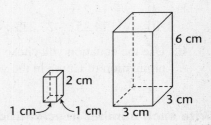

Evaluate each expression.

5. $\dfrac{4 \cdot 2^3 + 32}{\sqrt{15 + 1}}$

6. $\sqrt{\dfrac{2(-8) + 16(4) + 1}{25}}$

Graph each equation. Tell whether the graph is _linear_ or _nonlinear_.

7. $y = -2x + 2$

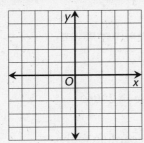

8. $y = x^2 - 3$

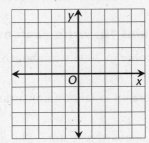

Find the slope of each line.

9.

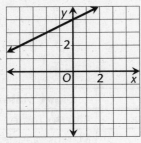

10.

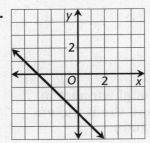

11. Find the height of the taller tree if the shorter tree is 8 ft tall.

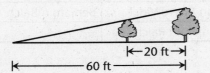

Name _____ Date _____

12. The scatter plot shows the population of China between 1972 and 1990. The year is on the *x*-axis and the population is on the *y*-axis (in millions).

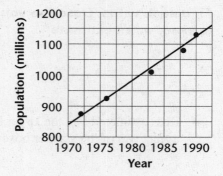

 a. Which equation best fits the line on the scatter plot?

   I. $y = 14.25x + 27{,}233$
   II. $y = 14.25x$
   III. $y = 14.25x - 27{,}233$

 b. Use the equation you chose in part (a) to predict the population of China in the year 2000.

Write each number in scientific notation.

13. In 2005, there were about 2,150,000 college degrees earned in the United States.

14. In 2010, it is estimated that there will be about 78,000,000 family households in the United States.

For Questions 15 and 16, write each number in decimal notation.

15. The national income in 2005 was about $1.024 \cdot 10^{13}$.

16. The U.S. membership in labor unions was $1.54 \cdot 10^{7}$ people in 2006.

17. Tanya works in a department store. She gets paid weekly according to the following formula: $p = \$20 + 5.35h$, where p is the total pay and h is the number of hours she works. Explain how she can use the formula to find her wage if she works 15 hours in a week.

The table shows the gold medal winners in the Men's Olympic Slalom and Giant Slalom competitions from 1988 to 2006.

18. Make a Venn diagram that includes the winners listed. Use the categories Slalom and Giant Slalom.

19. Which skiers have won both events?

20. How many skiers won a gold medal in either the Slalom or the Giant Slalom?

Slalom	Giant Slalom
Alberto Tomba	Alberto Tomba
F. C. Jagge	Markus Wasmeier
T. Stangassinger	Herman Maier
Hans-Petter Buraas	Stephen Eberharter
Jean-Pierre Vidal	Benjamin Raich
Benjamin Raich	

Math Thematics, Book 3
Teacher's Resource Book, Modules 3 and 4

Name _____ Date _____

1. Simplify $-\sqrt{400}$.
  a. 20   **b.** 14.1
  c. −20   **d.** −160000

7. Solve $-0.5 = 0.3x + 0.4$.
  a. 4   **b.** 3
  c. −4   **d.** −3

2. In 1991, there were 19,900,000 people who did job-related work at home. Express this number in scientific notation.
  a. $19.9 \cdot 10^6$ **b.** $1.99 \cdot 10^7$
  c. $0.199 \cdot 10^8$ **d.** $199 \cdot 10^7$

8. In 2020, the projected world population will be $7.6 \cdot 10^9$ people. Express this number in decimal form.
  a. 7,600,000,000   **b.** 760,000,000
  c. 76,000,000,000   **d.** 760,000,000,000

3. What is the value of $\dfrac{4 + 2(8) + 4^2}{\sqrt{9 + 16}}$?
  a. $\dfrac{36}{7}$ **b.** $\dfrac{64}{7}$
  c. $\dfrac{36}{5}$ **d.** $\dfrac{64}{5}$

9. What is the value of x in the equation $32.6 = \dfrac{x}{4.2} - 15.4$?
  a. 201.6   **b.** 4.1
  c. 11.4   **d.** 20.16

4. Which of the following equations has a graph that is nonlinear?
  a. $y = -0.5x + 4$ **b.** $y = 12x^2 + 10$
  c. $y = 4$ **d.** $y = -81x$

10. What is the value of x in $6.4 = -3.3x - 8.2$? Round to the nearest hundredth.
  a. 4.42   **b.** −0.54
  c. −4.42   **d.** 0.54

5. The flagpole in the diagram is 20 feet tall and is used to measure the height of a tree. Find the height of the tree.

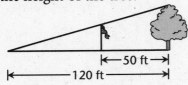

  a. 14.3 ft   **b.** 48 ft
  c. 40 ft   **d.** 34.3 ft

11. Find the slope of the fitted line below.

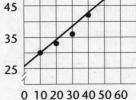

  a. $\dfrac{1}{3}$ **b.** $\dfrac{1}{2}$ **c.** 2   **d.** 3

6. According to the Venn diagram, how many students have a dog or a cat?

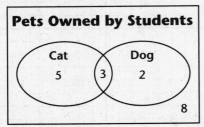

  a. 10   **b.** 8   **c.** 5   **d.** 3

12. Which is the perpendicular bisector of chord $\overline{AB}$?

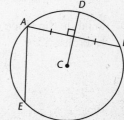

  a. $\overline{AB}$ **b.** $\overline{AE}$ **c.** $\overline{CD}$ **d.** $\overline{CB}$

Module Performance Assessment
For use after Module 3

The three lines on the graph below intersect and form a triangle.

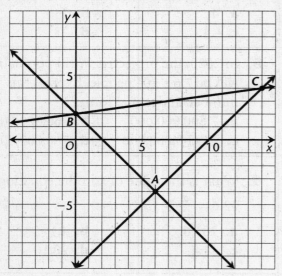

1. What type of triangle do the lines form?

2. Match one of these equations to each line.

   Equation 1: $7y = x + 14$

   Equation 2: $y = -x + 2$

   Equation 3: $y = x + 10$

   Equation 4: $y = x - 10$

3. What is the slope of line AC?

4. Graph the lines $y = -x - 5$ and $7y = x + 29$.

5. Use the lines in your graph from Exercise 4 to create a triangle that is similar to $\triangle ABC$ but is not congruent to $\triangle ABC$.

6. What is the slope of the line you drew in Exercise 5?

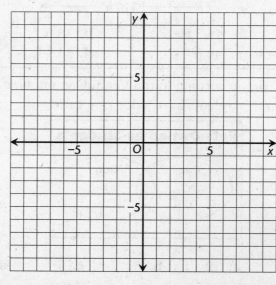

Contents

Book 3	Teacher's Resources for Module 4

Inventions

Name _____   Date _____

1. The diameter of a circle is 8 cm. Which of the following is the best estimate of its circumference?   (Sec. 1)

   A. 12.56 cm   **B.** 25.12 cm   **C.** 50.24 cm   **D.** 200.96 cm

2. The diameter of a circle is 8 cm. What is its area?   (Sec. 1)

   A. 4π cm^2 **B.** 8π cm^2 **C.** 16π cm^2 **D.** 64π cm^2

3. The radius of the base of a right circular cylinder is 7 in. and its height is 4 in. To the nearest square inch, the surface area of the cylinder is   (Sec. 2)

   A. 330 in.^{2} **B.** 396 in.^{2} **C.** 484 in.^{2} **D.** 616 in.^{2}

4. Find the ratio of the surface area to the volume for the cylinder at the right. Use 3.14 for π.   (Sec. 2)

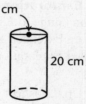

For each line, find the slope and the *y*-intercept. Then write an equation for the line in slope-intercept form.   (Sec. 3)

5.

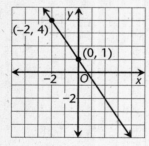

6.

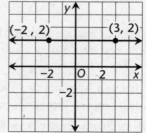

7. Write the numbers in order from least to greatest.   (Sec. 4)

   $\frac{5}{8}$, $0.6\overline{3}$, $0.62\overline{5}$, 0.63, $\frac{19}{30}$

Name _____   Date _____

Module Diagnostic Test

For use before Module 4

Solve each equation.   (Sec. 4)

8. $\frac{3}{5}x - 8 = 32$ **9.** $-9.6 = -1.2x + 24$

10. A legislative committee has 6 members.   (Sec. 5)

    a. How many ways can a chairperson and vice-chairperson be selected?

    b. How many subcommittees consisting of 2 people can be formed?

11. The authorization code used when making credit card purchases on the Internet   (Sec. 6)
is a randomly assigned 3-digit number such as 147.

    a. How many different authorization codes are possible?

    b. What is the probability that the last digit is 7?

    c. What is the probability that all three digits are different?

    d. What is the probability that the first digit is not 0?

The Math Gazette
Inventions

Sneak Preview!

Over the next several weeks in our mathematics class, we will find surface area and volume, investigate slope and the slope-intercept form of an equation, work with rational numbers, use the counting principle, and find permutations and combinations while completing a thematic unit on Inventions. Some of the inventions we will be discussing are:

▶ tin cans

▶ television

▶ Braille alphabet

▶ combination locks

▶ Egyptian hieroglyphs for writing numbers

Ask Your Student

What does the ratio of surface area to volume measure? (Sec. 2)

Which number in the equation $y = -3x + 2$ represents the slope of the line? the y-intercept? (Sec. 3)

What is a rational number? (Sec. 4)

What is the difference between a permutation and a combination of a group of objects? (Sec. 5)

Connections

Social Studies:
Students will learn about such inventions as the tin can, television, and combination locks. They may be interested in learning more about these inventions and their inventors. Encyclopedias, the Internet, or other reference works could be used as sources of information. Discuss recent inventions such as computer microchips and cell phones that have been important in our lives.

Literature:
Students will read an excerpt from *Seeing Fingers: The Story of Louis Braille*, by Etta DeGering. Some students may be interested in reading the book and making a report to the class.

Science:
Many important inventions are the result of scientific research. Encourage your student to look for articles in newspapers and magazines about scientific discoveries and their practical applications. Possible topics include medicine, computers, the environment, and space exploration.

E² Project

Following Section 2, students will have about one week to complete the Extended Exploration (E²), *Getting the Most Out of a Can*. In this project, students will use problem-solving skills to construct a cylinder with the greatest volume using an $8\frac{1}{2}$ in. × 11 in. sheet of paper.

Students might need the following material for the project:

▶ scissors, ruler, compass

▶ tape

▶ calculator

Module Project

After completing the module, students will explore a technique the ancient Egyptians may have used to move the massive stone blocks that form the Pyramids of Giza. Students will use the mathematics they have learned to design and build ramps and cylinders and use them to move small objects.

Inventions

Section Title	Mathematics Students Will Be Learning	Activities
1: Perfect Pancakes	◆ finding the circumference and area of a circle ◆ finding the volumes of prisms, cylinders, and spheres ◆ exploring the effect changing a linear dimension has on area or volume	◆ use data to develop a formula for circumference ◆ comparing the diameters and volumes of spheres made of clay
2: Can Do!	◆ finding the surface area of a cylinder ◆ finding and interpreting surface area to volume ratios	◆ construct a cylinder ◆ measure diameters and heights of cans ◆ calculate efficiency ratios
3: Color My World	◆ finding and interpreting slopes ◆ identifying the slopes of horizontal and vertical lines ◆ identifying the *y*-intercept of a line ◆ writing the equation of a line in slope-intercept form	◆ graph lines to determine slopes and *y*-intercepts
4: Writing Numbers	◆ identifying rational numbers ◆ using repeated notation for repeating decimals ◆ solving equations containing rational numbers	◆ explore Egyptian fractions ◆ investigate a problem from the Moscow Papyrus
5: Reading is Believing	◆ using the counting principle ◆ finding permutations ◆ finding combinations	◆ draw tree diagrams ◆ draw Braille symbols
6: Lock It Up!	◆ using the counting principle to find probabilities	◆ solve the duplicate key problem

Activities to do at Home

- ◆ Discuss inventions that have influenced you and others in your family the most and explain why. (After Sec. 2)

- ◆ Search for "hieroglyphs" on the Internet and visit some of the sites to learn more about reading and writing hieroglyphs. (After Sec. 4)

- ◆ Keep a record of where and how Braille is used in public places. (After Sec. 5)

Related Topics

You may want to discuss these related topics with your student:

 Package designs

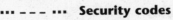 **Security codes**

 Egyptian pyramids and hieroglyphs

Name _____   Problem _____

MODULE 4 Teacher Assessment Scales
For use with Module 4

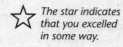
☆ *The star indicates that you excelled in some way.*

 Problem Solving

❶ ❷ ❸ ❹ ❺ ☆→

❶ You did not understand the problem well enough to get started or you did not show any work.

❸ You understood the problem well enough to make a plan and to work toward a solution.

❺ You made a plan, you used it to solve the problem, and you verified your solution.

 Mathematical Language

❶ ❷ ❸ ❹ ❺ ☆→

❶ You did not use any mathematical vocabulary or symbols, or you did not use them correctly, or your use was not appropriate.

❸ You used appropriate mathematical language, but the way it was used was not always correct or other terms and symbols were needed.

❺ You used mathematical language that was correct and appropriate to make your meaning clear.

 Representations

❶ ❷ ❸ ❹ ❺ ☆→

❶ You did not use any representations such as equations, tables, graphs, or diagrams to help solve the problem or explain your solution.

❸ You made appropriate representations to help solve the problem or help you explain your solution, but they were not always correct or other representations were needed.

❺ You used appropriate and correct representations to solve the problem or explain your solution.

 Connections

❶ ❷ ❸ ❹ ❺ ☆→

❶ You attempted or solved the problem and then stopped.

❸ You found patterns and used them to extend the solution to other cases, or you recognized that this problem relates to other problems, mathematical ideas, or applications.

❺ You extended the ideas in the solution to the general case, or you showed how this problem relates to other problems, mathematical ideas, or applications.

 Presentation

❶ ❷ ❸ ❹ ❺ ☆→

❶ The presentation of your solution and reasoning is unclear to others.

❸ The presentation of your solution and reasoning is clear in most places, but others may have trouble understanding parts of it.

❺ The presentation of your solution and reasoning is clear and can be understood by others.

Content Used: _____   **Computational Errors:** Yes ☐ No ☐

Notes on Errors: _____

Math Thematics, Book 3
Teacher's Resource Book, Modules 3 and 4

Name _____   Problem _____   **4-7**

 Student Self-Assessment Scales
For use with Module 4

▭ *If your score is in the shaded area, explain why on the back of this sheet and stop.*   ☆ *The star indicates that you excelled in some way.*

 Problem Solving

❶   ❷   ❸   ❹   ❺   ☆

I did not understand the problem well enough to get started or I did not show any work.

I understood the problem well enough to make a plan and to work toward a solution.

I made a plan, I used it to solve the problem, and I verified my solution.

 Mathematical Language

❶   ❷   ❸   ❹   ❺   ☆

I did not use any mathematical vocabulary or symbols, or I did not use them correctly, or my use was not appropriate.

I used appropriate mathematical language, but the way it was used was not always correct or other terms and symbols were needed.

I used mathematical language that was correct and appropriate to make my meaning clear.

 Representations

❶   ❷   ❸   ❹   ❺   ☆

I did not use any representations such as equations, tables, graphs, or diagrams to help solve the problem or explain my solution.

I made appropriate representations to help solve the problem or help me explain my solution, but they were not always correct or other representations were needed.

I used appropriate and correct representations to solve the problem or explain my solution.

 Connections

❶   ❷   ❸   ❹   ❺   ☆

I attempted or solved the problem and then stopped.

I found patterns and used them to extend the solution to other cases, or I recognized that this problem relates to other problems, mathematical ideas, or applications.

I extended the ideas in the solution to the general case, or I showed how this problem relates to other problems, mathematical ideas, or applications.

 Presentation

❶   ❷   ❸   ❹   ❺   ☆

The presentation of my solution and reasoning is unclear to others.

The presentation of my solution and reasoning is clear in most places, but others may have trouble understanding parts of it.

The presentation of my solution and reasoning is clear and can be understood by others.

4 Warm-Up Exercises
For use with Section 1

1. State the length of the diameter of the circle.

8.5 in.

2. State the length of the radius of the circle.

3. State the dimensions of the figure.

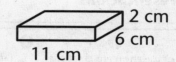

2 cm
6 cm
11 cm

4. Which of the objects shown are

   a. 1-dimensional?

   b. 2-dimensional?

   c. 3-dimensional?

ANSWERS

1. 8.5 in.   2. 4.25 in.   3. 11 cm by 6 cm by 2 cm   4. a. neither the circle nor the prism (but the radius, diameter, and length of one edge of the prism are each 1-dimensional)   b. the circle   c. the prism

Name _____   Date _____

Spheres and Volume (Use with Question 21(b) on page 237.)

Directions You will need modeling clay.

a. To simulate an *Aebleskiver*, use clay to make two spheres that are the same size. Cut one in half and measure the diameter. Record the diameter in the table. This is Sphere 1.

b. Roll the other sphere into a cylinder and cut it in half. Roll one of the halves into a sphere. Cut it open and compare its diameter to the original sphere's diameter.

c. Measure the new sphere's diameter and record it in the table. This is Sphere 2.

d. Cut the remaining cylinder in half again to obtain one-fourth of the original. Roll the one-fourth piece into a sphere. Compare the new sphere's diameter to the original. Repeat part (c) for this new sphere. This is Sphere 3.

e. Continue the process of cutting the cylinder in half, rolling it into a sphere and recording information in the table, until you obtain a sphere with a diameter that is half the original sphere.

Sphere	Volume (Fraction of the original sphere)	Length of Diameter (in cm)
1	1	
2	$\frac{1}{2}$	
3	$\frac{1}{4}$	

Name _____   Date _____

Practice and Applications
For use with Section 1

For use with Exploration 1

1. Find the exact circumference of a circle with the given radius or diameter.

   a. $d = 15$ cm   **b.** $r = 4$ in.   **c.** $d = 2.3$ m

2. Approximate the circumference of each circle in Exercise 1. Use $\pi = 3.14$.

3. **a.** How far would a bicycle with 30 inch tires travel in one complete turn of its wheels?

   b. How many turns would the smallest bicycle with tire diameter 0.76 inches have to make to go the same distance?

4. A certain single mirror telescope has a diameter of 19 feet 8 inches. What is the circumference of a circle with that diameter?

5. Find the exact area of a circle with the given radius or diameter.

   a. $r = 11$ ft   **b.** $d = 20$ cm   **c.** $d = 7$ in.

6. Approximate the area of each circle in Exercise 5. Use $\pi = 3.14$.

7. Lance is looking for a lamp for his night table. He finds a lamp with a circular base that has a diameter of 10 in.

   a. Approximate the area of the table that the lamp would cover.

   b. If the lamp would cover about $\frac{1}{3}$ of the table, about what size (in square inches) is the table?

   c. Lance decides to purchase a lamp with a circular base that has a diameter of 6 in. Determine the area of the base of this lamp.

   d. About what fraction of the table would the lamp from part (c) cover?

   (continued)

Math Thematics, Book 3
Teacher's Resource Book, Modules 3 and 4

Name _____   Date _____

MODULE 4 Practice and Applications
For use with Section 1

For use with Exploration 2

8. Find the volume of each figure. Use $\pi = 3.14$.

a.
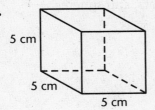
5 cm
5 cm
5 cm

b.
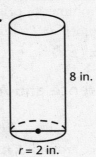
8 in.
$r = 2$ in.

c.
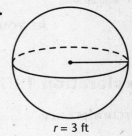
$r = 3$ ft

Find the volume of each cylinder. Use $\pi = 3.14$.

9. $r = 4$ cm
$h = 12$ cm

10. $r = 5.2$ cm
$h = 5.2$ cm

11. $r = 18$ cm
$h = 10$ cm

Find the volume of each rectangular prism. Use $\pi = 3.14$.

12. $l = 18$ cm
$w = 18$ cm
$h = 8$ cm

13. $l = 7$ cm
$w = 9$ cm
$h = 6$ cm

14. $l = 6$ cm
$w = 12.5$ cm
$h = 10$ cm

Find the exact volume of a sphere with the given dimension.

15. $r = 30$ in.

16. $r = 4.2$ m

17. $d = 12$ ft

18. a. A cereal box measures $2\frac{3}{4}$ inches by $8\frac{1}{4}$ inches by 12 inches. Find its volume.

b. The box contains 15 ounces of cereal, the "net weight." Why doesn't the manufacturer list the volume on the box?

19. One of the largest cheeses ever made was 14.5 ft long, 6.5 ft wide, and 6 ft high. It was made in January of 1964 for the World's Fair in New York. It toured the country and was displayed until 1968, when it was cut up and sold.

a. Estimate the volume of the cheese.

b. The whole cheese weighed 34,591 pounds. Find the weight of one cubic foot of cheese. Round to the nearest tenth of a cubic foot.

c. Use your answer to part (b) to help you estimate how many 8 ounce blocks of cheese fit into a volume of 1 cubic foot.

Name _____   Date _____

Study Guide
For use with Section 1

Perfect Pancakes   Circumference, Area, and Volume

GOAL   **LEARN HOW TO:** • find the circumference and area of a circle
• find the volumes of prisms, cylinders, and spheres
AS YOU: • interpret scatter plots
• investigate eating records

Exploration 1: Finding Circumference and Area

Circumference

The **circumference** of a circle is the distance around it. π is the ratio of the circumference of a circle to its diameter. π is approximately equal to 3.14. The formula for finding the circumference is $C = \pi d$.

Example

Find the circumference of a circle with a diameter of 6 cm. Use 3.14 for π.

Sample Response

$C = \pi d$ ← Use the formula for circumference.
$\approx (3.14)(6)$ ← Substitute 6 for d and 3.14 for π.
$= 18.84$

The circumference is about 18.84 cm.

Area

The **area** of a circle is the number of square units of surface the figure covers. To find the area of a circle when you know its radius, use the formula $A = \pi r^2$.

Example

Find the area of a circle with a radius of 1.7 cm. Use 3.14 for π to find an approximate area.

Sample Response

Exact Area

$A = \pi r^2$
$= \pi (1.7)^2$
$= \pi (2.89)$
$= 2.89\pi$

The exact area is 2.89π cm^2.

Approximate Area

$A = \pi r^2$
$= \pi (1.7)^2$
$= (3.14)(2.89)$
≈ 9.0746

An approximate area is 9.0746 cm^2.

Name _____ Date _____

Exploration 2: Finding Volume

Prisms and Cylinders

A **polyhedron** is a 3-dimensional object made up of flat surfaces, or *faces*, that are polygons.

A **prism** is a *polyhedron* in which two of the faces, the **bases**, are congruent and parallel. The other faces are parallelograms. In a rectangular prism, the bases are rectangles. In this book, all the prisms are right prisms, so all faces other than the bases will be rectangles.

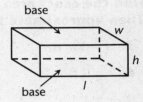

To find the volume of a right prism, use the formula volume = area of the base × height or $V = Bh$, where B is the area of a base and h is the height.

A **cylinder** is a 3-dimensional figure that has a curved surface and two parallel, congruent bases. In this book, all the cylinders are circular cylinders. That means their bases are circles.

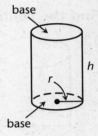

To find the volume of a cylinder, use the formula volume = area of the base × height. Since the area of a circle is $A = \pi r^2$, the volume of a circular cylinder can be written as $V = \pi r^2 h$.

Spheres

A **sphere** is a 3-dimensional figure made up of a set of points that are an equal distance from a given point, called the center.

To find the volume of a sphere, use the formula $V = \frac{4}{3}\pi r^3$, where r is the radius.

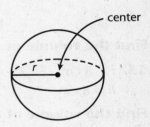

Name _____ Date _____

Study Guide: Practice & Application Exercises
For use with Section 1

Exploration 1

1. Find the circumference of a dinner plate whose diameter is 25.6 cm.

2. A bicycle whose wheels have a diameter of 15 in. was ridden a distance of 235.5 in. How many complete turns did the wheels make?

Find the exact area of a circle with the given radius or diameter. Then approximate the area of each circle.

3. $d = 18$ cm   4. $r = 5$ in.   5. $d = 3.8$ m

6. $r = 9$ ft   7. $d = 30$ cm   8. $d = 6$ in.

9. $r = 1.4$ m   10. $d = 8$ ft   11. $r = 7$ cm

Exploration 2

Find the volume of each figure.

12.
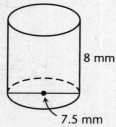
8 mm
7.5 mm

13.
4 m
6 m
2 m

14.
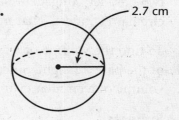
2.7 cm

Find the volume of a cylinder with the given dimensions.

15. $r = 8$ cm   16. $r = 3$ cm   17. $r = 12$ cm
    $h = 8$ cm $h = 11$ cm $h = 9$ cm

Find the volume of a rectangular prism with the given dimensions.

18. $l = 13$ cm   19. $l = 12$ cm   20. $l = 2$ cm
    $w = 13$ cm $w = 10$ cm $w = 3$ cm
    $h = 6$ cm $h = 5$ cm $h = 15$ cm

Find the exact volume of a sphere with the given dimension. Then approximate the volume of each sphere.

21. $r = 17$ ft   22. $r = 4.5$ in.   23. $d = 3$ m

Math Thematics, Book 3
Teacher's Resource Book, Modules 3 and 4

Name _____   Date _____

Quick Quiz
For use after Section 1

1. Find the circumference of a circle with radius 12 cm. Use $\pi = 3.14$.

2. Find the exact area of a circle with diameter 25 in.

3. Find the volume of each figure. Round answers to the nearest tenth.
   Use $\pi = 3.14$.

   a.
   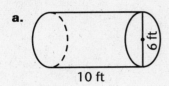
   6 ft
   10 ft

   b.
   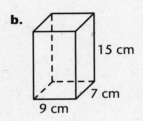
   15 cm
   7 cm
   9 cm

   c.
   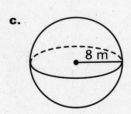
   8 m

4. Tobin's mother pours out the same amount of soup for him and his brother Mac. Tobin's is poured into a bowl and Mac's into a cup. Write an argument using mathematics from this section that explains why Tobin's soup cools faster than his brother's.

Name _____   Date _____

**Find the area of a circle with the given dimension.
Use 3.14 for π.**

1. radius: 3 cm

2. radius: 6.2 ft

3. diameter: 12 in.

4. Find the surface area of a cube with edges 11 cm long.

5. Find the volume of a cube with edges 11 cm long.

ANSWERS

1. 28.26 cm^2 2. 120.7016 ft^2 3. 113.04 in.^2 4. 726 cm^2 5. 1331 cm^3

Math Thematics, Book 3
Teacher's Resource Book, Modules 3 and 4

MODULE 4   **LABSHEET** **2A**

Cylinders (Use with Questions 12 and 13 on page 249.)

Directions Find the surface area, *S.A.*, and the volume, *V*, of each cylinder.
Use 3.14 for π.

A.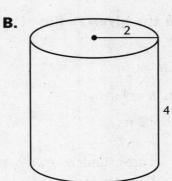

B.

C.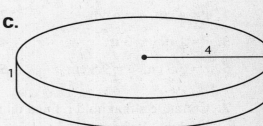

16

S.A. = _____   *S.A.* = _____

V = _____   *V* = _____

D.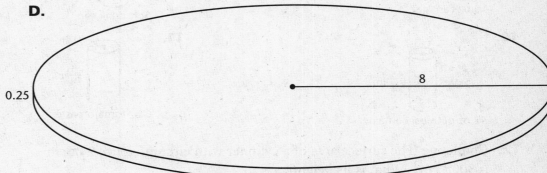

S.A. = _____   *S.A.* = _____

V = _____   *V* = _____

Name _____ Date _____

Practice and Applications

For use with Section 2

For use with Exploration 1

Find the surface area of the cylinder with the given radius and height. Use π = 3.14.

1. $r = 4$ cm, $h = 6$ cm

2. $r = 1$ m, $h = 1$ m

3. $r = 1$ ft, $h = 3$ ft

4. $r = 1.8$ m, $h = 9$ m

5. $r = 3.5$ cm, $h = 9.8$ cm

6. $r = 8$ ft, $h = 2$ ft

7. Containers that hold refined oil for use in cars are cylinders. Find the surface area of a cylinder that has a diameter of 30 feet and a height of 25 feet.

Find the surface area of the following commonly used cylinders. Use π = 3.14.

8.

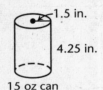

1.5 in.

4.25 in.

15 oz can

9.

6.5 cm

12 cm

Soft drink can

10.

5 in.

$9\frac{3}{4}$ in.

42 oz oatmeal container

11.

1 in.

$3\frac{1}{4}$ in.

6 oz tomato paste

12. Challenge The surface area of a cylinder with circumference 24π cm is 300π cm^2. What is its height?

(continued)

Name _____ Date _____

Practice and Applications
For use with Section 2

For use with Exploration 2

Find the ratio of surface area to volume for each can.
Use π = 3.14.

13.
1.5 in.
4 in.

14.
3 in.
12 in.

15.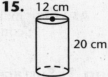
12 cm
20 cm

16. Use your answers for Exercises 13–15 to rank the cans shown above from the most efficient to the least efficient.

Find the ratio of surface area to volume for each of the following commonly used cylinders. Use π = 3.14.

17.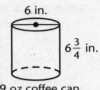
6 in.
$6\frac{3}{4}$ in.
39 oz coffee can

18.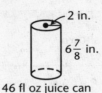
2 in.
$6\frac{7}{8}$ in.
46 fl oz juice can

19.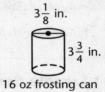
$3\frac{1}{8}$ in.
$3\frac{3}{4}$ in.
16 oz frosting can

20. Challenge A 10 ounce soup can has a diameter of $2\frac{1}{2}$ inches and a height of $3\frac{7}{8}$ inches, while a 19 ounce soup can has a diameter of 3 inches and a height of $4\frac{7}{8}$ inches.

   a. Which can is more efficient?

   b. Find the ratio of the volumes of the soup cans.

   c. How does the ratio of the volumes of the soup cans compare to the ratio of the weights of the soup cans? Show the ratio of the weights.

   d. How does the ratio of the volumes of the soup cans compare to the ratio of the diameters of the soup cans? Show the ratio of the diameters.

   e. Writing Use the answers to parts (a)–(d) to determine which soup can you would manufacture if you had the opportunity. Explain your choice.

Name _____   Date _____

Study Guide
For use with Section 2

Can Do!   Working with Cylinders

GOAL   **LEARN HOW TO:** • find the surface area of a cylinder
• find and interpret the ratio of a cylinder's surface area to its volume

AS YOU: • make a paper can
• compare the efficiency of different cans

Exploration 1: Surface Areas of Cylinders

Finding Surface Area of a Cylinder

The **surface area** of a 3-dimensional figure is the combined area of the figure's outer surfaces. The surface area, *S.A.*, of a cylinder with radius *r* and height *h* is given by the formula $S.A. = 2\pi r^2 + 2\pi rh$.

Example

Find the surface area of the cylinder shown.

Sample Response

$S.A. = 2\pi r^2 + 2\pi rh$
$= 2\pi(1.3)^2 + 2\pi(1.3)(5)$
$\approx 10.6 + 40.8$
≈ 51.4

The cylinder's surface area is about 51.4 in.^{2}

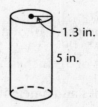
1.3 in.

5 in.

Example

Find the surface area of a cylinder with the given radius *r* and height *h*.

$r = 2$ cm, $h = 5.3$ cm

Sample Response

$S.A. = 2\pi r^2 + 2\pi rh$
$= 2\pi(2)^2 + 2\pi(2)(5.3)$
$\approx 25.12 + 66.568$
≈ 91.688

The cylinder's surface area is about 91.688 cm^2.

Math Thematics, Book 3
Teacher's Resource Book, Modules 3 and 4

Name _____   Date _____   **4-21**

Exploration 2: Surface Area and Volume

Comparing Surface Area to Volume

For a container (such as a can) with surface area *S.A.* and volume *V*, the ratio $\frac{S.A.}{V}$ is a measure of the object's *efficiency*. The smaller this ratio, the more efficient the object. An *efficient* can is one that uses a small amount of metal compared to the amount of food or drink it holds.

Example

Rank the cans shown from most efficient to least efficient.

A. 3 in. 16 in.

B. 4 in. 9 in.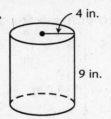

C. 2 in. 36 in.

Sample Response

First Find the ratio $\frac{S.A.}{V}$ for each can.

A. $\frac{S.A.}{V} \approx \frac{357.96}{452.16}$ ≈ 0.79

B. $\frac{S.A.}{V} \approx \frac{326.56}{452.16}$ ≈ 0.72

C. $\frac{S.A.}{V} \approx \frac{477.28}{452.16}$ ≈ 1.06

Then Put the ratios in order from least to greatest.

$0.72 < 0.79 < 1.06$

Can B, Can A, Can C

The ratio $\frac{S.A.}{V}$ is the least for Can B and the most for Can C, so Can B is the most efficient, Can C is the least efficient, and Can A is between the other two.

Name _____   Date _____

Study Guide: Practice & Application Exercises
For use with Section 2

Exploration 1

**Find the surface area of the cylinder with the given radius *r*
and height *h*.**

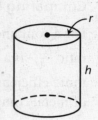

1. *r* = 3 ft, *h* = 5 ft   **2.** *r* = 6 mm, *h* = 12 mm

3. *r* = 1.2 cm, *h* = 3.4 cm   **4.** *r* = 7.7 yd, *h* = 6.9 yd

5. *r* = 16 m, *h* = 10 m   **6.** *r* = 40 ft, *h* = 45 ft

7. Mental Math Use mental math to estimate the surface area of a
circular cylinder with a radius of 1 ft and a height of 10 ft. Use $\pi \approx 3$.

Exploration 2

Find the ratio of surface area to volume for each cylinder.

8.   **9.**   **10.**

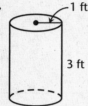   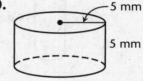

11.   **12.**   **13.**

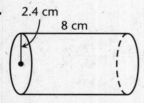   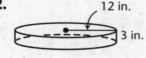   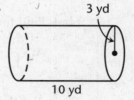

14. A can of salmon has a height of 4 cm and a radius of 4 cm. A can of
tomato paste has a height of 8.5 cm and a radius of 2.5 cm. A can of
corn has a height of 11 cm and a radius of 3.5 cm.

   a. Find the ratio of surface area to volume for each can.

   b. Use your answers to part (a) to rank the cans from most efficient to
   least efficient.

Name _____   Date _____   **4-23**

 **Quick Quiz**
For use after Section 2

1. Find the surface area of a cylinder with a radius of 8 cm and a height of 7 cm. Use 3.14 for π.

2. Find the ratio of the surface area to volume of a cylinder with a radius of 6 cm and a height of 6 cm. Use 3.14 for π.

3. The surface area of a cylinder is 900 cm^2. Find a radius and a height that this cylinder could have. Use 3.14 for π.

Solution Guide: Textbook E²

For use with E² on textbook page 257

Getting the Most Out of a Can

Students' solutions to this open-ended problem will vary. All of the *Math Thematics Assessment Scales* can be used to assess students' solutions. If students have difficulty getting started, you may want to remind them of the relationship between the circumference of the circle forming the base and the length of the rectangle forming the body of the cylinder.

It appears that the greatest volume can be obtained with the following cylinder layout, where the circumference of the base is 11 in.

The volume of this cylinder is about 48.1 in.³

$$V = \pi r^2 h$$

$$V = \pi \left(\frac{3.5}{2}\right)^2 (5)$$

$$V \approx 48.1$$

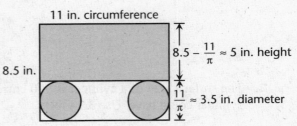

In the layout, when the area of the base is decreased and the height of the cylinder is increased, the volume decreases.

The volume of this cylinder is about 47.5 in.³

$$V = \pi r^2 h$$

$$V = \pi \left(\frac{2.7}{2}\right)^2 (8.3)$$

$$V \approx 47.5$$

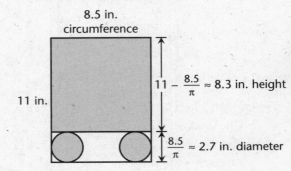

The table below shows that when using the horizontal layout as in the first figure, the volume increases as the circle is enlarged.

Circumference	Radius of base	Cylinder height	Volume ($\pi r^2 h$)
9	1.4324	5.635	36.322
10	1.592	5.317	42.335
10.9	1.735	5.03	47.57
11	1.7507	4.9986	48.131

Circles with greater area can be constructed when the layout is designed diagonally on the paper as shown here. (Note that when the parallelogram is rolled up it forms an open-ended cylinder.)

However, the height is too small to produce a greater volume.

$$V = \pi r^2 h$$

$$V = \pi \left(\frac{3.8}{2}\right)^2 (3.40) \approx 38.6 \text{ in.}^3$$

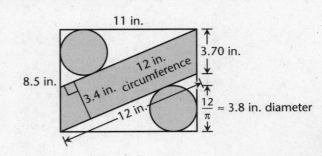

Alternate E²
For use with Module 4

Wet Paint

The Situation

While riding your bike, you accidentally rode across some wet paint.

The Problem

Suppose the paint spill was 4 in. wide where you rode across it. If you continue to ride in a straight line, what will the track left by the bike's tires look like? Your bike tire has a diameter of 26 in. (You can ignore the pattern of the tire tread.)

Something to Think About

- How much of the bike's tires will be covered with paint?

- What are some assumptions you can make about wet paint on a moving object?

- Which problem solving strategies can you use to help solve this problem?

- How can you test your conclusions?

4 in.

Present Your Results

Describe what you did to solve the problem. Show any problem solving strategies you used. Explain why you think your answer is correct.

Solution Guide: Alternate E²

For use with Module 4

Wet Paint

There is only one solution to this problem, but students' approaches to it will vary. All of the *Math Thematics Assessment Scales* can be used to assess students' solutions, but the problem does not provide much opportunity to make connections, so you may not want to score students on the Connections Scale.

You can introduce the problem by asking students if they have ever seen the track left by the tires on a car after it was driven across freshly painted lines for a crosswalk or lane dividers. If they have, they can describe what they saw and then brainstorm what information they would need to give a more precise description of the track. Make sure the students understand that they are investigating the track left by the bicycle tires, not the pattern in the tread of the tires.

Partial Solution

The circumference of a 26 in. diameter tire is approximately 82 in., and the track left by the tires would be:

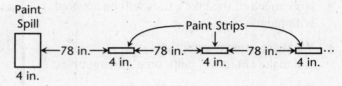

This solution can be generalized to a tire with any circumference C:

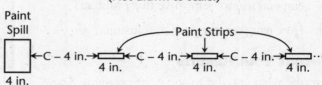

At some point in their solution, students should show that, regardless of the distance between the axles of the tires, if the tires have the same diameter, the strip left by the rear tire will overlay the strip left by the front tire. This can be shown with a model. The example at the right illustrates this for the case where the distance between the tires is $\frac{1}{2}$ the circumference, C, of the tires. The radius on each tire indicates the location of the paint on the tire.

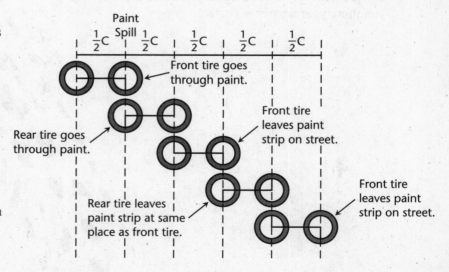

Students can extend the problem by describing the track left by the tires when the diameter of the rear wheel is a fraction $\left(\frac{1}{2}, \frac{1}{3}, \text{etc.}\right)$ of the diameter of the front tire.

Name _____   Date _____

Warm-Up Exercises
For use with Section 3

1. Plot each point on the axes at the right.

   a. $(-1, 4)$ **b.** $(2, -2)$

2. Draw the line through these two points.

3. Name another point on the line.

4. Name the point where the line crosses

   a. the x-axis.   **b.** the y-axis.

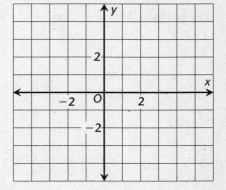

ANSWERS

1–2. 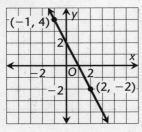   3. Sample Response: $(3, -4)$ 4. a. $(1, 0)$ b. $(0, 2)$

Name _____ Date _____

Graph of Black-and-White TV Sales

(Use with Questions 4–9 on pages 259–260.)

Directions Use the graph to complete the table.

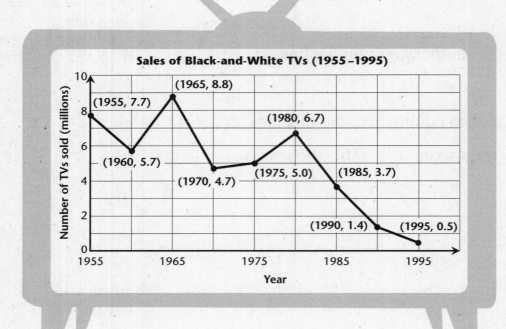

Period	Rise	Run	Slope of graph	Does graph slant *up* or *down* from left to right?	Are TV sales *increasing* or *decreasing*?
1955–1960	–2	5	–0.4	down	decreasing
1960–1965					
1965–1970					
1970–1975					
1975–1980					
1980–1985					
1985–1990					
1990–1995					

Math Thematics, Book 3
Teacher's Resource Book, Modules 3 and 4

Name _____   Date _____

Practice and Applications

For use with Section 3

For use with Exploration 1

Find the slope of each line.

1.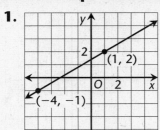

2.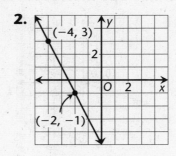

3.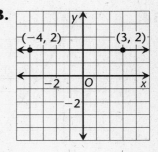

Find the slope of the line through the given points. You may find it helpful to plot the points and draw a line through them first.

4. (3, 5) and (5, –2)

5. (4, 6) and (8, 6)

6. (–2, –3) and (6, 0)

7. (–5, 7) and (–5, 9)

8. (2, –4) and (6, –4)

9. (0, 2) and (0, –2)

10. Use the lines shown.

    a. Which line has a positive slope?

    b. Which line has a negative slope?

    c. Which line has a slope of zero?

    d. Which line has an undefined slope?

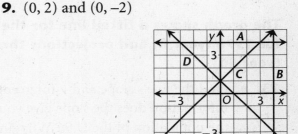

The percentage of adult males who were overweight increased dramatically from 1960 to 1994, as shown in the graph at the right.

11. Estimate the rate of increase from 1980 to 1994.

12. Find the rate of increase in the percent of males who were overweight from 1976 to 1980.

13. Use slope to find the average rate of increase from 1960 to 1994.

Percentage of Males Who Were Overweight

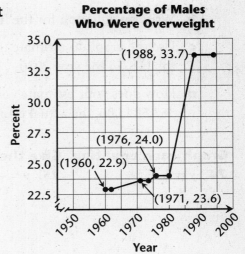

(continued)

Name _____   Date _____

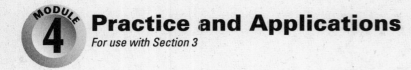

For use with Exploration 2

For each line, write an equation in slope-intercept form.

14.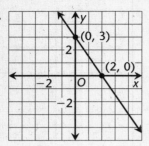

15.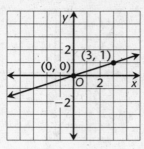

16.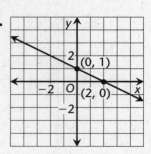

Write an equation in slope-intercept form for the line through the given points. You may find it helpful to plot the points and draw a line through them first.

17. $(0, 6)$ and $(1, 4)$ 18. $(0, 3)$ and $(4, 9)$ 19. $(-5, 5)$ and $(0, 5)$

20. $(1, 6)$ and $(3, 2)$ 21. $(3, 7)$ and $(8, 9)$ 22. $(-4, 0)$ and $(0, 5)$

The graph shows a fitted line for the U.S. population for 1990 (year 0) and projections through the year 2040 (year 50).

23. **a.** Find the line's slope and y-intercept. What information does the slope give you about the population of the U.S.? What information does the y-intercept give you about the population?

   b. Write an equation for the line.

   c. Use the graph to estimate the population of the U.S. in the year 2030.

   d. How does your estimate compare with 363,584,000, the actual estimate?

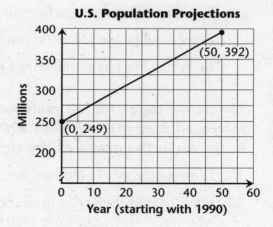

U.S. Population Projections

Graph each equation. Give the slope of each line.

24. $y = 4$ 25. $y = -3$ 26. $x = 2$ 27. $x = -1$

Math Thematics, Book 3
Teacher's Resource Book, Modules 3 and 4

Name _____ Date _____

MODULE 4 Study Guide
For use with Section 3

Color My World   Slopes and Equations of Lines

GOAL **LEARN HOW TO:** • find and interpret positive and negative slopes
• identify slopes of horizontal and vertical lines
• identify the *y*-intercept of a line
• write an equation of a line in slope-intercept form

AS YOU: • investigate TV sales
• model sales of DVD players and VCRs

Exploration 1: Exploring Slope

Finding and Comparing Slopes

The *slope* of a line is the ratio that measures the steepness of the line.

$$\text{slope} = \frac{\text{rise}}{\text{run}} = \frac{\text{vertical change}}{\text{horizontal change}}$$

The slope of a line can be *positive*, *negative*, *zero*, or *undefined*.

Example

Positive slope

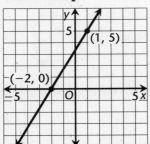

$$\frac{\text{vertical change}}{\text{horizontal change}} = \frac{5 - 0}{1 - (-2)} = \frac{5}{3}$$

Negative slope

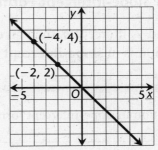

$$\frac{\text{vertical change}}{\text{horizontal change}} = \frac{4 - 2}{-4 - (-2)} = \frac{2}{-2} = -1$$

Zero slope

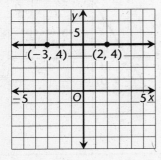

$$\frac{\text{vertical change}}{\text{horizontal change}} = \frac{4 - 4}{2 - (-3)} = \frac{0}{5} = 0$$

Undefined slope

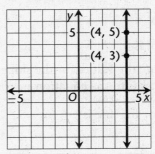

$$\frac{\text{vertical change}}{\text{horizontal change}} = \frac{5 - 3}{4 - 4} = \frac{2}{0} \leftarrow \text{undefined}$$

Math Thematics, Book 3
Teacher's Resource Book, Modules 3 and 4   **4-31**

Name _____   Date _____

Exploration 2: Slope-Intercept Form

Finding *y*-intercepts

The **y-intercept** of a line is the *y*-coordinate of the point where the line crosses the *y*-axis.

> **Example**
>
> Name the *y*-intercept of the line shown.
>
> The line crosses the *y*-axis at the point (0, 5).
>
> The *y*-intercept is 5.
>
>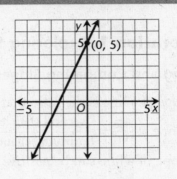

Writing Equations in Slope-Intercept Form

If a line has slope *m* and *y*-intercept *b*, then an equation of the line is $y = mx + b$. This equation is in **slope-intercept form**.

> **Example**
>
> Write an equation in slope-intercept form for the line shown.
>
> ■ **Sample Response** ■
>
> **First** Find the slope and the *y*-intercept.
>
> $$slope = \frac{5 - 0}{0 - (-3)} = \frac{5}{3}$$
>
> The *y*-intercept is 5.
>
> **Then** Substitute the values for the slope *m* and the *y*-intercept *b* into the equation $y = mx + b$.
>
> An equation for the line is $y = \frac{5}{3}x + 5$.
>
>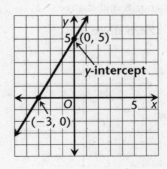

Name _____   Date _____

Study Guide: Practice & Application Exercises

For use with Section 3

Exploration 1

Find the slope of the line through the given points. You may find it helpful to plot the points and draw a line through them first.

1. (0, 3) and (2, 5)   **2.** (−2, 6) and (9, 5)   **3.** (−5, 7) and (−1, −2)

4. (−3, 5) and (5, 5)   **5.** (0, 6) and (9, 0)   **6.** (−2, 6) and (−2, 5)

Use the lines shown for Exercises 7–9.

7. Which line has a positive slope?

8. Which line has a negative slope?

9. Which line has an undefined slope?

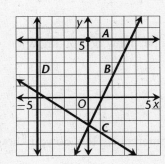

Exploration 2

For each line, write an equation in slope-intercept form.

10.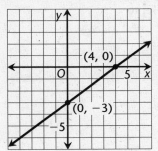

11.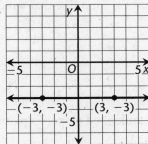

12.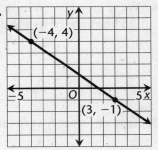

Write an equation in slope-intercept form for the line through the given points. You may find it helpful to plot the points and draw a line through them first.

13. (1, 4) and (4, 6)   **14.** (0, 3) and (3, 0)   **15.** (−1, −1) and (1, 1)

Graph each equation. Give the slope of each line.

16. $x = -2$ **17.** $y = -4$ **18.** $x = 3$

Math Thematics, Book 3
Teacher's Resource Book, Modules 3 and 4   **4-33**

Name _____   Date _____

Quick Quiz
For use after Section 3

Your mother asks you to baby-sit your younger brother while she runs errands. She agrees to pay you $5 just to stay with him and then $3 for every hour she is gone. Use the table below to answer the following questions.

1. Write an equation in slope-intercept form for this data.

Baby-sitting Earnings	
x = hours worked	y = wages earned
0	5
1	5 + 3(1) = 8
2	5 + 3(2) = 11
3	5 + 3(3) = 14
4	5 + 3(4) = 17
5	5 + 3(5) = 20

2. What is the slope? How do you know?

3. What is the y-intercept? How do you know?

4. Write an equation in slope-intercept form for a line that would be parallel to the line created by the data above.

5. True or False: A vertical line has an undefined slope. Explain.

Math Thematics, Book 3
Teacher's Resource Book, Modules 3 and 4

Name _____   Date _____

Mid-Module Quiz
For use after Section 3

1. Which of the objects at the right has the greater volume. How do you know?

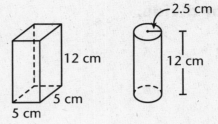

2. The radius of a cylinder is increased to 10 times its original length. Which of the following is true?

   A. The volume increases to 100 times the original volume.

   B. The volume increases to 10 times the original volume.

   C. The volume increases to 20 times its original volume.

   D. The volume is not affected.

3. The diameter of the base of a circular swimming pool is 15 ft.

   a. Find the exact circumference of the swimming pool.

   b. How could you find the approximate circumference of the pool?

4. Find the approximate surface area of a cylinder with a radius of 4 cm, and a height of 5 cm. Use 3.14 for π.

5. Find the ratio of surface area to volume for the cylinder at the right.

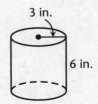

For each line, find the slope, the *y*-intercept, and an equation of the line.

6.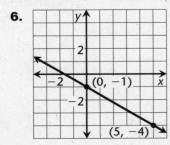

7.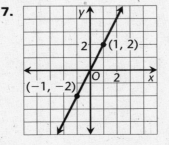

8.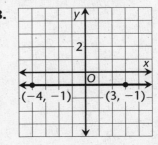

Warm-Up Exercises

For use with Section 4

Multiply or divide.

1. $18 \div \frac{1}{3}$

2. $\frac{3}{5} \cdot \frac{1}{5}$

3. $9 \div 1\frac{1}{2}$

Solve each equation.

4. $3x + 4 = -2$

5. $-3x + 7 = 10$

6. $5 - x = -11$

ANSWERS

1. 54   2. $\frac{3}{25}$ 3. 6   4. −2   5. −1   6. 16

Name _____   Date _____

Practice and Applications
For use with Section 4

For use with Exploration 1

Write each rational number as the quotient of two integers.

1. 0.40

2. $\sqrt{36}$

3. $\sqrt{\dfrac{25}{64}}$

4. 3.5

5. $8\dfrac{1}{2}$

6. $\sqrt{0.25}$

Write each rational number as a repeating or a terminating decimal.

7. $\dfrac{7}{12}$

8. $\dfrac{2}{3}$

9. $\sqrt{100}$

10. $\dfrac{2}{9}$

11. $7\dfrac{3}{4}$

12. $\sqrt{\dfrac{36}{64}}$

13. Write each rational number as a terminating or repeating decimal. Then write the numbers in order from least to greatest.

    a. $\dfrac{7}{36}$

    b. $\dfrac{8}{32}$

    c. $-2\dfrac{1}{3}$

14. Challenge $\dfrac{2}{7}$ is a rational number because it can be written as the quotient of two integers.

    a. How many decimal places repeat?

    b. Give another rational number with a large number of decimal places that repeat.

15. Write the repeating decimals below in order from greatest to least. Explain your thinking.

    a. $0.15\overline{4}$ $0.1\overline{54}$ $0.\overline{154}$ $0.\overline{15}$

    b. $2.\overline{3}$ $2.\overline{32}$ $2.3\overline{2}$ $2.33\overline{2}$

(continued)

Practice and Applications
For use with Section 4

For use with Exploration 2

Solve each equation.

16. $\frac{2}{3}n = 18$

17. $12 = \frac{3}{4}y$

18. $1\frac{3}{5}x = 100$

19. $\frac{3}{4}x + 12 = 20$

20. $32 = \frac{2}{5}k - 16$

21. $3\frac{2}{3}r - 2 = 30$

22. $\frac{6}{7}m + \frac{2}{7} = \frac{8}{7}$

23. $\frac{4}{9}n + \frac{2}{3} = \frac{2}{3}$

24. $1\frac{4}{5}y - \frac{1}{8} = \frac{7}{8}$

25. $4x - 8 = 32$

26. $-0.5x - 1.75 = 8.25$

27. $\frac{5}{8}x = -\frac{3}{4}$

28. $-\frac{3}{4}x + \frac{1}{4} = \frac{11}{8}$

29. $3.75x + 7 = -26.75$

30. $\frac{3}{4}x + 8 = \frac{15}{16}$

31. To quickly convert from kilograms to pounds, multiply the number of kilograms by 2.2 to get an estimate of the number of pounds.

   a. Write an equation to convert from kilograms to pounds.

   b. 18 kilograms is about how many pounds?

   c. 14 pounds is about how many kilograms?

32. The equation $Y = 1.308M$ can be used to convert from cubic meters to cubic yards, where Y is the number of cubic yards and M is the number of cubic meters.

   a. What is the number of cubic yards for 18 cubic meters?

   b. What is the number of cubic meters for 20 cubic yards?

Name _____   Date _____

Study Guide
For use with Section 4

Writing Numbers   Rational Numbers

GOAL   **LEARN HOW TO:** • recognize the characteristics of rational numbers
• use notation for repeating decimals
• solve equations containing rational numbers

AS YOU: • explore ratios and Egyptian fractions
• investigate a problem from the Moscow Papyrus

Exploration 1: Rational Numbers

A **rational number** is a number that can be written in the form $\frac{a}{b}$, where a and b are integers and $b \neq 0$. When written as a decimal, a rational number is either a **terminating decimal** (a decimal containing a limited number of digits) or a **repeating decimal** (a decimal containing a digit or group of digits that repeats forever). The repeating digit or digits in a repeating decimal are shown using an *overbar*.

Example

Write each rational number as a quotient of two integers. Then use your answers to write each rational number as a terminating or repeating decimal.

a. $3\frac{2}{5}$ **b.** $\sqrt{25}$ **c.** $-1\frac{13}{15}$

Sample Response

a. $3\frac{2}{5} = \frac{17}{5}$ ← Multiply 5 by 3 and add 2.

$\phantom{3\frac{2}{5}} = 3.4$ ← Divide 17 by 5.

b. $\sqrt{25} = \frac{5}{1}$ ← Find the square root of 25.

$\phantom{\sqrt{25}} = 5$

c. $-1\frac{13}{15} = -\frac{28}{15}$

$\phantom{-1\frac{13}{15}} = -1.8666666...$

$\phantom{-1\frac{13}{15}} = -1.8\overline{6}$ ← Add an overbar above 6 to show that it repeats.

Study Guide
For use with Section 4

Exploration 2: Equations with Rational Numbers

You can solve equations that contain rational numbers. The rules for multiplying and dividing negative rational numbers are the same as the rules for multiplying and dividing negative integers.

Example

Solve $-3.5y = 70$.

■ Sample Response ■

$$-3.5y = 70$$

$$-3.5y \div (-3.5) = 70 \div (-3.5) \qquad \leftarrow \text{Divide both sides by } (-3.5)$$

$$y = -20$$

Example

Solve $-\frac{2}{3}x + 8 = 22$.

■ Sample Response ■

$$-\frac{2}{3}x + 8 = 22$$

$$-\frac{2}{3}x + 8 - 8 = 22 - 8 \qquad \leftarrow \text{Subtract 8 from both sides.}$$

$$-\frac{2}{3}x = 14$$

$$-\frac{2}{3}x \div \left(-\frac{2}{3}\right) = 14 \div \left(-\frac{2}{3}\right) \qquad \leftarrow \text{Divide both sides by } -\frac{2}{3}.$$

$$-\frac{2}{3}x \cdot \left(-\frac{3}{2}\right) = 14 \cdot \left(-\frac{3}{2}\right) \qquad \leftarrow \text{Multiply both sides by } -\frac{3}{2}, \text{ the reciprocal of } -\frac{2}{3}.$$

$$x = -21$$

Check: $-\frac{2}{3}x + 8 = 22$

$$-\frac{2}{3}(-21) + 8 \overset{?}{=} 22 \qquad \leftarrow \text{Replace } x \text{ with } -21.$$

$$14 + 8 \overset{?}{=} 22$$

$$22 = 22 \checkmark$$

Name _____   Date _____

Study Guide: Practice & Application Exercises
For use with Section 4

Exploration 1

Write each rational number as a quotient of two integers.

1. -2

2. $4\frac{1}{6}$

3. 0.20

4. $\frac{3}{8}$

5. $-1\frac{1}{4}$

6. $\sqrt{49}$

Write each rational number as a terminating or repeating decimal.

7. $\frac{5}{12}$

8. $-2\frac{1}{9}$

9. $1\frac{3}{5}$

10. $\frac{23}{25}$

11. $-5\frac{2}{11}$

12. $1\frac{3}{4}$

13. Write your answers for Exercises 7–12 in order from least to greatest.

Exploration 2

Solve each equation.

14. $\frac{1}{3}x = -5$

15. $4 = 8 + \frac{3}{4}m$

16. $\frac{4}{5}y - \frac{3}{10} = \frac{2}{10}$

17. $\frac{4}{9} + \frac{7}{18}t = \frac{5}{9}$

18. $\frac{3}{8}r = 39$

19. $11 = \frac{4}{11}f - 44$

20. $2.6x - 1.3 = 22.1$

21. $-7.3x + 8 = -0.03$

22. $8\frac{3}{4} = -\frac{7}{9}x$

23. Vanessa is shopping for furniture in a catalog. The store she likes uses metric measurements in the item descriptions. To find the measurements in inches, Vanessa multiplied the number of centimeters by 0.39.

    a. Write an equation Vanessa could have used to estimate measurements in inches given measurements in centimeters.

    b. About how many centimeters is 60 in.?

    c. About how many inches is 125 cm?

    d. How would she convert inches to centimeters?

Name _____   Date _____

4 Quick Quiz
For use after Section 4

1. Which of the following represents the decimal number 0.8575757...?

   A. $0.\overline{857}$ **B.** $0.8\overline{57}$ **C.** $0.85\overline{7}$ **D.** $0.8\overline{57}$ **E.** $0.\overline{8}57$

Write each rational number as a terminating or repeating decimal.

2. $3\frac{2}{3}$

3. $\frac{3}{8}$

Multiply or divide.

4. $-\frac{4}{5} \cdot \frac{3}{2}$

5. $-6 \div \left(-\frac{5}{2}\right)$

6. $18.6 \div -0.3$

Solve each equation.

7. $3x + 1.2 = -4.8$

8. $-\frac{1}{2}x + \frac{3}{4} = \frac{7}{8}$

9. $-0.8x - 6.4 = 14.4$

Math Thematics, Book 3
Teacher's Resource Book, Modules 3 and 4

Name _____   Date _____   **4-43**

 **Warm-Up Exercises**
For use with Section 5

Multiply.

1. 2^7

2. $6 \cdot 5 \cdot 4 \cdot 3 \cdot 2 \cdot 1$

State the number of possible choices for each event.

3. choosing a letter of the alphabet

4. choosing a one-digit number

5. choosing a female from your class

ANSWERS
   1. 128   2. 720   3. 26   4. 10   5. Answers will vary.

Math Thematics, Book 3
Teacher's Resource Book, Modules 3 and 4   **4-43**

MODULE 4   **LABSHEET** 5A

Gabriel's Sentence (Use with Question 1 on page 284.)

Directions Gabriel's Braille sentence is shown below. The sentence has been reversed.

○●	●○	●○	○●	●○	○○	●●	○●	●●	○○	●○
●○	●●	○●	●●	●●	○○	●○	○○	○○	○○	○●
○○	○●	○○	○●	●○	○○	○●	○○	○○	○○	○○
letter	letter	letter	letter	letter	space	letter	letter	letter	space	letter

- Place this labsheet on a soft surface, such as a pad of paper. Press down on each solid dot in Gabriel's sentence with the tip of a pen. You should press hard enough to indent the paper without tearing it.

- Turn the labsheet over so that the printed dots are not shown. You should be able to feel raised dots where you indented the paper. Move your hand from left to right across the dots without looking at them. Use the Braille alphabet on page 284 of your book to determine what Gabriel's sentence says.

- For each letter in Gabriel's sentence, list the positions of the *raised* dots. Do not just use the diagram at the top of the page, as it is reversed. (For example, according to the Braille cell diagram below, the positions of the dots in the letter ●● are 1, 3, 4, and 5.)
  ○●
  ●○

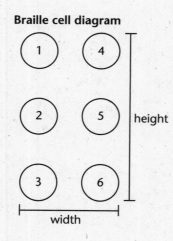

Braille cell diagram

Math Thematics, Book 3
Teacher's Resource Book, Modules 3 and 4

Name _____   Date _____

Tree Diagram (Use with Questions 10 and 11 on pages 288 and 289.)

Directions Use the Braille diagram below to complete the tree diagram.

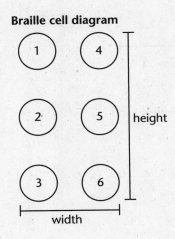

Braille cell diagram

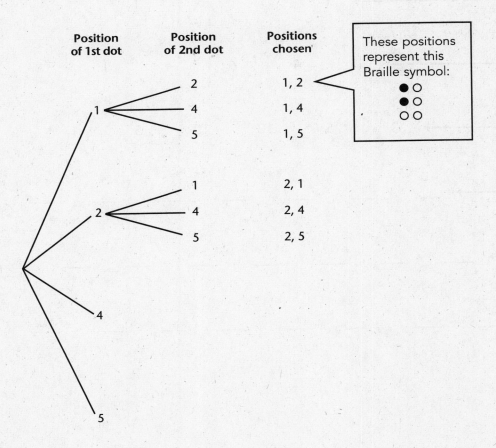

Name ______________________ Date ______________

MODULE 4 **LABSHEET 5C**

Pascal's Triangle (Use with Exercise 26 on page 295.)

Directions Complete rows 6–8 of Pascal's triangle.

row 0 → 1

row 1 → 1 1

row 2 → 1 2 1

row 3 → 1 3 3 1

row 4 → 1 4 6 4 1

row 5 → 1 5 10 10 5 1

row 6 → ___ ___ ___ ___ ___ ___ ___

row 7 → ___ ___ ___ ___ ___ ___ ___ ___

row 8 → ___ ___ ___ ___ ___ ___ ___ ___ ___

Name _____   Date _____

Practice and Applications

For use with Section 5

For use with Exploration 1

1. Sundaes at a certain ice cream shop are available in 5 flavors: vanilla, strawberry, chocolate, raspberry, and butter pecan. There are also three toppings available: fudge, nuts, and fruit.

   a. Draw a tree diagram showing the different choices available for the ice cream and the toppings for a sundae.

   b. In how many ways can you choose one ice cream flavor and one topping for the sundae?

2. Maurice wants to buy a new stereo system and a new video game system. He limits his choices to 3 stereo systems and 4 video game systems. In how many ways can he choose a stereo system and a video game system?

3. Tanya rents all newly released movies. There are 10 movies on the "new release" list. In how many orders can she rent the movies if she chooses one at a time?

Find the number of permutations of the letters in each word.

4. GO

5. BUMPER

6. SEAT

7. TRUNK

8. CAR

9. GASOLINE

10. In professional football, there are 4 teams per division. In how many orders can the teams in a division finish at the end of the regular football season?

11. In basketball, 12 different teams participate in a holiday tournament. In how many orders can the teams finish the tournament?

12. A car repair person is supposed to do a "10-point inspection," or check 10 different items or settings in the engine or car. In how many different orders can the inspection be done?

13. Marjean made a list of 7 errands to do. In how many different orders can she do her errands?

14. Marty Jung rearranges the letters of his name to form a password for his computer. In how many different orders can he rearrange the letters of his name?

(continued)

Name _____   Date _____

Practice and Applications
For use with Section 5

For use with Exploration 2

15. Mr. Junge grouped his class into 6 groups. Each day, two groups have to put homework problems on the board. How many combinations of two groups can be chosen?

16. Calin has strawberries, watermelon, grapes, pineapple, and peaches. How many combinations of fruits can she put in a salad if she uses:

    a. exactly 1 kind of fruit?   **b.** exactly 2 kinds of fruit?

    c. exactly 3 kinds of fruit?   **d.** exactly 4 kinds of fruit?

    e. exactly 5 kinds of fruit?   **f.** at least 3 kinds of fruit?

17. Students in Mrs. Jacobs' class have to answer 3 out of 5 essays on a test. How many combinations of 3 essays can be chosen?

18. There are 8 different toppings available at Papa Joe's pizza restaurant.

    a. How many different pizzas can be made with two toppings?

    b. How many different pizzas can be made with three toppings?

    c. A "supreme" pizza has six toppings. How many different pizzas can be made with six toppings?

19. A clothing inspector selects 2 pairs of socks at random from each box to check the production quality. How many different combinations of socks can be chosen from a box of 12 pairs?

20. Challenge Suppose Randy chooses 4 letters of his name to form a password for his computer.

    a. How many branches would a tree diagram have that shows the number of combinations of 4 letters?

    b. How many permutations of 3 letters can he make with the 4 letters he has chosen?

Math Thematics, Book 3
Teacher's Resource Book, Modules 3 and 4

4-48

Name _____   Date _____

Study Guide
For use with Section 5

Reading is Believing   Counting Techniques

GOAL   **LEARN HOW TO:** • use the counting principle to count numbers of choices
• find the number of permutations of a group of objects
• find numbers of combinations

AS YOU: • work with Braille symbols
• investigate the first ten letters of the Braille alphabet

Exploration 1: Counting and Permutations

Using a Tree Diagram to Count Choices

You can use a tree diagram to count choices in a given situation.

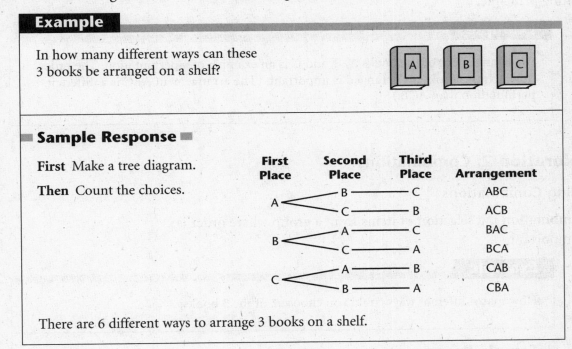

Using the Counting Principle

The **counting principle** states that the total number of ways that a
sequence of decisions can be made is the product of the number of
choices for each decision.

Example

Use the counting principle to determine the number of ways the three books in the
above Example can be arranged.

(continued on next page)

Study Guide
For use with Section 5

Sample Response

Number of arrangements	=	Number of choices for 1st place	×	Number of choices for 2nd place	×	Number of choices for 3rd place
		3		2		1

= 6

Finding Permutations

A **permutation** of a group of items is an arrangement of the items in a definite order. You can find the number of permutations using the counting principle.

Example

An arrangement of the books A, B, and C is an example of a permutation. The order in which the books are arranged is important. (The arrangement ABC is a different permutation than ACB.)

Exploration 2: Combinations

Finding Combinations

A **combination** is a selection of items from a group where order is not important.

Example

How many different ways could you choose 2 of the 3 books?

Sample Response

1st Choice	2nd Choice	Selection
A	B	AB
	C	AC
B	A	BA
	C	BC
C	A	CA
	B	CB

The selections with the same letters are the same combination. BA is the same as AB, CA is the same as AC, and CB is the same as BC. There are 3 possible combinations.

Name _____   Date _____

Study Guide: Practice & Application Exercises
For use with Section 5

Exploration 1

1. Elizabeth has to choose 2 students, one for first place and one for second place, from the 5 who qualified to receive a scholarship. She wonders how many arrangements are possible. Use a tree diagram to determine how many.

2. Use the counting principle to answer Exercise 1.

3. Why is Exercise 1 an example of a permutation?

Find the number of permutations of the letters in each word.

4. BE

5. TRY

6. CAUGHT

7. STAMP

8. DEAL

9. MONTHLY

10. Deena is assembling a gift basket for her aunt's birthday. She can choose from 12 different fruits, 8 kinds of cheese, 5 types of crackers, 4 flavors of jam, and 2 kinds of sausage. If a basket contains exactly 1 of each type of food, how many different gift baskets could she possibly create?

Exploration 2

11. How many ways can you choose 3 CDs from a group of 5?

12. How many different 2 card hands can be dealt from a stack of 6 cards?

13. A flower bouquet comes with any 3 of these flowers: rose, carnation, lily, iris. How many different bouquets are possible?

14. Why are Exercises 11–13 examples of combinations?

15. Peter wants to make a sauce flavored with herbs. He has oregano, thyme, rosemary, and sage in his spice cabinet. How many combinations of herbs can Peter use in his sauce if he uses each of the following?

   a. exactly 1 type of herb
   b. exactly 2 types of herbs
   c. exactly 3 types of herbs
   d. at least 2 types of herbs

Name _____   Date _____

Quick Quiz

For use after Section 5

1. A restaurant has 8 entrees, 4 salads, and 3 desserts. In how many ways can a customer order an entree, a salad, and a dessert?

2. In how many different ways can the letters of the word LENGTH be arranged?

3. For your class party, you are given the task of choosing 3 CDs from a set of 8 CDs. How many different combinations are possible?

Name _____   Date _____

Warm-Up Exercises

For use with Section 6

A box contains a red flag, a blue flag, a white flag, and a green flag. State the number of choices for each event.

1. In how many ways can the four flags be picked?

2. In how many ways can two flags be picked?

3. In how many ways can three flags be picked?

Write each fraction as a decimal rounded to the nearest hundredth.

4. $\dfrac{3}{7}$

5. $\dfrac{140}{253}$

ANSWERS

1. 24   2. 12   3. 24   4. 0.43   5. 0.55

Name _____ Date _____

Practice and Applications
For use with Section 6

For use with Exploration 1

For Exercises 1–3, suppose two number cubes are rolled and the number of sixes is recorded.

1. List all possible outcomes when two number cubes are rolled.

2. What is the probability of getting 0 sixes? 1 six? 2 sixes?

3. What is the probability of getting at least one six?

4. Your phone number is a 7-digit number (without the area code). The first three digits depend on your town, and the last 4 digits are chosen from the numbers 0–9.

    a. How many sequences are possible for the last four digits?

    b. What is the probability of getting a 1 or a 9 in the last digit?

    c. What is the probability of getting 2 zeros in the last two digits?

    d. What is the probability of getting 3 zeros in the last two digits?

    e. Suppose your entire phone number uses digits chosen from the numbers 0–9. How many sequences are possible for the seven digits?

5. Suppose two number cubes are rolled.

    a. How many outcomes are possible?

    b. How many outcomes have a sum of 9? 10?

    c. What is the probability that the sum of the numbers is 9 or 10?

6. **Open-ended** Suppose Randy chooses 3 letters of his name and other *characters* from the keyboard to complete his 4-character password for his computer (for example: "RNY@" is a possibility).

    a. Draw a tree diagram to find the number of combinations of 3 letters and other characters from the keyboard.

    b. What is the probability that he chose "RNY@" as his password?

Math Thematics, Book 3
Teacher's Resource Book, Modules 3 and 4

Study Guide
For use with Section 6

Lock It Up! Working with Probability

GOAL **LEARN HOW TO:** • use the counting principle to determine the probability of an event

AS YOU: • solve the duplicate key problem

Exploration 1: Probability and Counting

Finding Probability

You can use the counting principle to find some probabilities.

Example

What is the probability that rolling four 6-sided number cubes will result in four different numbers?

Sample Response

$$\text{Probability} = \frac{\text{Ways to roll different numbers}}{\text{Total ways to roll cubes}}$$

If different numbers are to be rolled, there are 6 numbers possible for the first number cube, 5 possible for the second number cube, 4 possible for the third number cube, and 3 possible for the fourth number cube.

$$\text{Probability} = \frac{6 \cdot 5 \cdot 4 \cdot 3}{6 \cdot 6 \cdot 6 \cdot 6}$$

Each number cube, when rolled has a total of 6 different outcomes.

$$= \frac{10}{36} \approx 0.28$$

The probability of rolling 4 number cubes and getting 4 different numbers is about 0.28.

MODULE 4

Study Guide: Practice & Application Exercises
For use with Section 6

Exploration 1

For Exercises 1–4, suppose two 6-sided number cubes are rolled and the outcomes are recorded.

1. List all the possible outcomes when 2 number cubes are rolled.

2. Tell the probability of each outcome.

   a. two 1's   **b.** a 2 and a 3   **c.** doubles

3. What is the probability of getting at least one 6?

4. What is the probability that both number cubes will be even numbers?

Suppose three spinners, with five equal-sized sectors labeled A, B, C, D, and E, are each spun once. Find the probability of each outcome.

5. all A's   6. all vowels

7. all consonants   8. no E's

9. a number   10. three letters

For Exercises 11–12, suppose a combination lock uses a 4-number key based on the numbers from 0 to 19.

11. How many possible keys are there for this type of lock?

12. What is the probability the lock could be opened on the first try?

13. Madison is playing a board game that involves rolling two 6-sided number cubes at the same time. To win the game, Madison must roll two numbers that have a sum of 10. What is the probability that Madison will win the game on her next roll?

Math Thematics, Book 3
Teacher's Resource Book, Modules 3 and 4

Name _____   Date _____

Quick Quiz
For use after Section 6

For Questions 1–3, suppose two coins are tossed and the number of heads is recorded.

1. List all the possible outcomes for tossing two coins.

2. What is the probability of getting
   a. two heads?

   b. one head?

   c. no heads?

3. What is the probability of getting at least one head?

For Questions 4–5, suppose a number code is made up using five digits chosen from the digits 0–9.

4. How many codes are possible?

5. What is the probability that the last digit will be a 0?

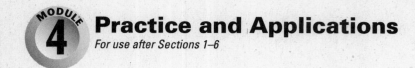

Practice and Applications

For use after Sections 1–6

For use with Section 1

1. Use $C = \pi d$ to find the diameter of a circle with a circumference of 45.9 mm. Use 3.14 for π.

2. The volume of a rectangular prism is 385 cm^3. The area of the base is 35 cm^2. What is the height of the prism?

Find the volume of each cylinder. Round your answers to the nearest hundredth.

3. $r = 5$ mm
$h = 6$ mm

4. $d = 2.4$ in.
$h = 8.9$ in.

5. $r = 3$ ft
$h = 12$ ft

For use with Section 2

6. Find the surface area of a cylinder that has a radius of 8 in. and a height of 12 in.

7. Find the surface area and the volume of a cube whose edges are 8 mm long.

8. Find the surface area of a cylinder whose radius is 2 in. and whose height is 10 in.

For use with Section 3

9. Give the slope and the y-intercept of the line with equation $y = -3x + 8$.

Write an equation in slope-intercept form of a line that has the given slope and y-intercept.

10. slope = 5, y-intercept = 4

11. slope = -3, y-intercept = -2

Graph each equation. Give the slope of each line.

12. $y = -3x + 3$

13. $y = 3x - 2$

14. $y = \frac{1}{2}x + 1$

(continued)

Name _____   Date _____   **4-59**

Practice & Applications

For use after Sections 1–6

For use with Section 4

Solve each equation.

15. $-\frac{3}{4}x = 21$

16. $50 = \frac{2}{5}g - 5$

17. $-22 = \frac{3}{2}y - \frac{1}{2}y$

Write each rational number as a terminating or repeating decimal.

18. $\frac{7}{11}$

19. $3\frac{4}{5}$

20. $-\frac{5}{6}$

For use with Section 5

21. Linda, Samuel, and Julio have been chosen as winners of a bike, CD player, and $100 savings bond. The winner of each prize will be determined by a random drawing. What is the probability that Linda will receive the bike? that Samuel will not receive the CD player?

22. Does counting the ways to choose 5 of 15 possible kinds of flowers for a bouquet involve permutations or combinations? Explain.

23. Jackie needs to choose 3 of 5 types of flowers to make an arrangement. How many combinations of 3 types of flowers can Jackie choose?

For use with Section 6

One popular game involves rolling four 6-sided number cubes. Find the probability of each outcome when rolling the number cubes.

24. all ones

25. all even numbers

26. all different numbers

27. all numbers greater than 4

28. no threes

29. all perfect squares

Name _____   Date _____

Ramp and Cylinders (Use with Questions 1–4 on page 304.)

Directions The diagrams below show a ramp and cylinders supporting a block.
The diameters of the cylinders decrease from one diagram to the next. Use the
diagrams to complete the table at the bottom of the page.

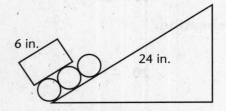

Cylinder diameter = 3 in.
Cylinder length = 12 in.

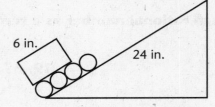

Cylinder diameter = 2 in.
Cylinder length = 12 in.

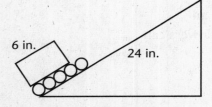

Cylinder diameter = 1.5 in.
Cylinder length = 12 in.

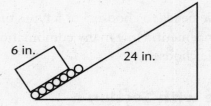

Cylinder diameter = 1 in.
Cylinder length = 12 in.

Cylinder diameter (in.)	Number of cylinders needed	Volume of each cylinder (in.³)	Combined volume of all cylinders (in.³)
3			
2			
1.5			
1			

Name _____   Date _____

Test Form A
For use after Module 4

Find the surface area of the cylinder with the given radius *r* and height *h*. Use π = 3.14.

1. $r = 4$ in., $h = 6$ in.   **2.** $r = 3.1$ cm, $h = 8$ cm

Find the ratio of surface area to volume for each cylinder. Use π = 3.14.

3.   4 in.
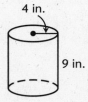
9 in.

4. 6 in.
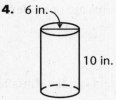
10 in.

5. Would the ratios in Questions 3 and 4 be affected if you found the exact surface area and volume for each cylinder? Explain.

6. Suppose you have two cans with the same dimensions as the cylinders in Questions 3 and 4. Which can is more efficient?

For each line, find the slope and the *y*-intercept. Then write an equation for the line in slope-intercept form.

7.
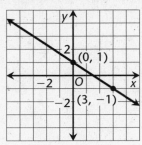

8.
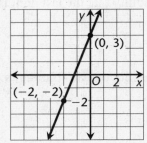

9. Write the numbers in order from least to greatest.

$\frac{3}{4}$, $0.\overline{75}$, $0.72\overline{5}$, 0.725, $\frac{13}{16}$

Test Form A
For use after Module 4

Solve each equation.

10. $8 = \frac{3}{4}x$

11. $0.25 = -0.5x - 0.75$

12. A uniform at a private school consists of a choice of 3 skirts, 4 shirts, 2 sweaters, and 5 pairs of socks.

   a. How many different uniforms are possible?

   b. In how many different orders can the shirts hang in a student's closet?

   c. All of one student's socks are in a drawer. How many combinations of 2 socks can be chosen?

13. Banks that have telephone banking often ask customers to use the last four digits of their social security number as an identification code. The last four digits are randomly assigned numbers from 0–9.

   a. How many different identification codes are possible?

   b. What is the probability that the last digit is a 0?

   c. What is the probability that all four digits are the same?

   d. What is the probability that the last two digits are 9s?

Math Thematics, Book 3
Teacher's Resource Book, Modules 3 and 4

Name _____   Date _____

 **Test Form B**
For use after Module 4

Find the surface area of the cylinder with the given radius *r* and height *h*. Use π = 3.14.

1. *r* = 3 in., *h* = 8 in.

2. *r* = 4.2 cm, *h* = 7.1 cm

Find the ratio of surface area to volume for each cylinder. Use π = 3.14.

3.
3 in.
7 in.

4.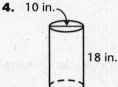
10 in.
18 in.

5. Would the ratios in Questions 3 and 4 be affected if you found the exact surface area and volume for each cylinder? Explain.

6. Suppose you have two cans with the same dimensions as the cylinders in Questions 3 and 4. Which can is more efficient?

For each line, find the slope and the *y*-intercept. Then write an equation for the line in slope-intercept form.

7.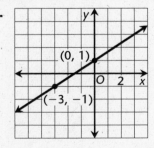
(0, 1)
O 2 x
(−3, −1)

8.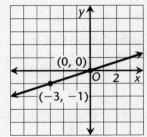
(0, 0)
O 2 x
(−3, −1)

9. Write the numbers in order from least to greatest.

$0.\overline{37}, \frac{5}{16}, 0.37\overline{5}, \frac{3}{8}, 0.37$

Test Form B
For use after Module 4

Solve each equation.

10. $25 = \dfrac{2}{5}x$

11. $0.36 = -1.2x - 0.72$

12. A menu at a restaurant consists of 5 entrees, 4 desserts, and 2 salads.

    a. In how many ways can a customer order an entree, a salad, and a dessert?

    b. In how many different ways can the desserts be listed in order on the menu?

    c. The restaurant offered a special of 2 entrees for the price of one. How many combinations of 2 entrees can be chosen?

13. Computer systems often require users to type in a log-in identification code. Suppose the code is a randomly assigned sequence of 5 letters of the alphabet.

    a. How many different identification codes are possible?

    b. What is the probability that the last letter is Z?

    c. What is the probability that all five letters are the same?

    d. What is the probability that the last two letters are AA?

Math Thematics, Book 3
Teacher's Resource Book, Modules 3 and 4

Name _____ Date _____

Standardized Test
For use after Module 4

1. Find the surface area of a cylinder with radius 5 cm and height 10 cm.
   a. 314 cm^2
   b. 471 cm^2
   c. 1256 cm^2
   d. 1570 cm^2

2. Choose the correct statement(s) below.

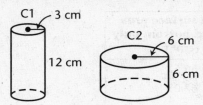

   I. $\frac{SA}{V}$ for C1 > $\frac{SA}{V}$ for C2

   II. $\frac{SA}{V}$ for C1 = $\frac{SA}{V}$ for C2

   III. $\frac{SA}{V}$ for C1 < $\frac{SA}{V}$ for C2

   a. I only
   b. II only
   c. III only
   d. not enough information

3. What is the value of x in the equation $\frac{3}{4}x - 24 = 32$?
   a. 0
   b. $10\frac{2}{3}$
   c. 42
   d. $74\frac{2}{3}$

4. Two number cubes are rolled. Find the probability that a sum of 5 or 6 is rolled.
   a. $\frac{1}{3}$
   b. $\frac{1}{4}$
   c. $\frac{1}{6}$
   d. $\frac{1}{9}$

5. Find the volume of a rectangular prism with length 18 cm, width 12 cm, and height 9 cm.
   a. 39 cm^3
   b. 1944 cm^3
   c. 6107 cm^3
   d. 17,496 cm^3

6. Find the volume of a cylinder with radius 9 cm and height 8 cm.
   a. 226 cm^3
   b. 648 cm^3
   c. 2035 cm^3
   d. 8143 cm^3

7. What is the value of x in the equation $0.72 = -0.9x - 5.4$?
   a. −14
   b. −6.8
   c. −5.2
   d. −1.4

8. Which of the following is an equation of the line graphed below?

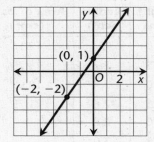

   a. $y = \frac{2}{3}x + 1$
   b. $y = \frac{3}{2}x + 1$
   c. $y = \frac{2}{3}x - 2$
   d. $y = -\frac{3}{2}x = 1$

9. Which of the following numbers is the greatest?
   a. $0.67\overline{6}$
   b. 0.67
   c. $0.\overline{67}$
   d. $\frac{2}{3}$

10. Two number cubes are rolled. Find the probability that the sum of the number cubes is 11.
   a. $\frac{1}{36}$
   b. $\frac{1}{18}$
   c. $\frac{1}{9}$
   d. $\frac{1}{6}$

11. How many permutations of the letters in the word "WIDTH" are there?
   a. 5
   b. 10
   c. 25
   d. 120

12. A circular lake has 980 miles of shoreline. Estimate its area.
   a. 1000 mi^2
   b. 3075 mi^2
   c. 76,400 mi^2
   d. 306,000 mi^2

Name _____   Date _____

Module Performance Assessment

For use after Module 4

A toy manufacturer wants to make a set of 10 nested cups for young children. Each cup in the set can fit inside the next larger cup, as shown at the right.

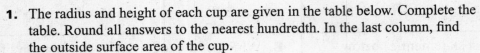

1. The radius and height of each cup are given in the table below. Complete the table. Round all answers to the nearest hundredth. In the last column, find the outside surface area of the cup.

Height (cm)	Radius (cm)	Area of base (cm²)	Volume (cm³)	Outside surface area sides and bottom only (cm²)
3.50	2	12.56	43.96	56.52
3.75	2.2	15.20	57.00	67.03
4.00	2.4	18.09	72.36	
4.25	2.6	21.23		
4.50	2.8			
4.75	3.0			
5.00	3.2			
5.25	3.4			
5.50	3.6			
5.75	3.8			

2. **a.** Which nested cup has the least outside-surface-area-to-volume ratio?

    b. What pattern do you notice about the ratios for the cups?

3. The toy manufacturer would like the nested cups colored so that each cup is a different color. Which colors might the manufacturer use? Why?

4. How many ways are there to color the 10 cups using the colors chosen in Exercise 3?

5. If a cup is chosen at random, what is the probability the cup has

    a. a volume less than 150 cm³?

    b. a surface area less than 150 cm²?

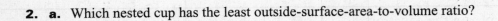

Math Thematics, Book 3
4-66 Teacher's Resource Book, Modules 3 and 4

Name _____ Date _____

Cumulative Test
For use after Modules 3 and 4

Find each value. Tell whether your answer is exact or an estimate.

1. $\sqrt{0.49}$

2. $-\sqrt{300}$

Evaluate each expression.

3. $\dfrac{2 \cdot 3^2 + 6}{3(4 - 10) + 15}$

4. $\sqrt{\dfrac{7(12) + 6(-8)}{2(8)}}$

5. Graph $y = -2x - 2$.

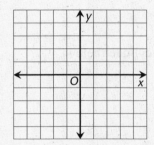

6. Which of the following equations have graphs that are nonlinear?

A. $x = 2$ **B.** $y = x^2 - 4$ **C.** $y = \sqrt{x}$ **D.** $y = \dfrac{2}{5}x - 6$

7. The scatter plot shows the number of computers shipped worldwide each year from 2001 through 2005. The year is on the x-axis and the number of computers is on the y-axis.

a. Which equation best fits the line on the scatter plot?

    I. $y = 25x + 90$
    II. $y = 25x$
    III. $y = 25x - 90$

b. Use the equation you chose in part (a) to predict the number of computers shipped in the year 2010.

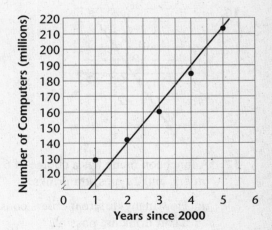

8. In 2010, there will be about 114,800,000 households in the United States. Write 114,800,000 in scientific notation.

9. In 1997, the value of 100-dollar bills in circulation was about 2.52×10^9 dollars. Write this number in decimal notation.

10. Find the height of the taller tree if the shorter tree is 12 ft tall.

Cumulative Test
For use after Modules 3 and 4

Solve each equation.

11. $-6y + 3.6 = -72$

12. $\frac{2}{3}x - 12 = 24$

13. The radius of the base of a cylinder is 4.1 cm and its height is 9.2 cm. Find the surface area of the cylinder. Use 3.14 for π and round the answer to the nearest tenth.

14. Find the ratio of surface area to volume for the cylinder below.

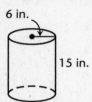

6 in.

15 in.

For each line, find the slope, the *y*-intercept, and an equation of the line.

15.

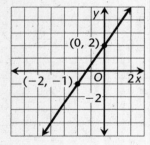

16.

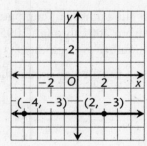

17. A luncheon menu has a choice of 6 types of sandwiches, 3 types of side orders, and 2 types soft drinks.

   a. How many different orders consisting of one sandwich, a side order, and a soft drink are possible?

   b. On special, two sandwiches of equal value can be bought for the price of one. How many different combinations of two sandwiches can be made?

18. A certain security code uses four randomly assigned digits from 0–9.

   a. How many different security codes are possible?

   b. What is the probability that the last digit is "0"?

Name _____   Date _____

Mid-Year Test
For use after Modules 1–4

Find each sum or difference.

1. $-12 + 8$

2. $4 + (-7) + 8$

3. $-10 - (-4)$

4. $-\frac{5}{6} + \frac{2}{3}$

5. $\frac{1}{5} - \frac{3}{4}$

6. $\frac{2}{5} - \left(-2\frac{1}{3}\right)$

Find each product or quotient.

7. $(8)(-6)$

8. $-3(-6)(-4)$

9. $-84 \div (-12)$

10. $\frac{-42}{-7}$

11. $\frac{65}{-5}$

12. $\frac{-27}{3}$

Evaluate each expression.

13. $\sqrt{81}$

14. $\frac{4^2}{3(-6) + 22}$

15. $\sqrt{\frac{25}{36}}$

16. $\frac{7(12) + 6(-8)}{2(8)}$

17. $|-8| - |-3|$

18. $|-8 - 3|$

Find each value. Tell whether your answer is exact or an estimate.

19. $\sqrt{0.64}$

20. $-\sqrt{200}$

21. $\sqrt{6.25}$

Use an equation to find each number or percent.

22. What is 62% of 84?

23. 8 is what percent of 160?

24. 9.75 is 25% of what number?

25. 90 is what percent of 60?

Evaluate each expression when $a = -6$, $b = -2$, and $c = 12$.

26. ab

27. $c \div b$

28. abc

Solve each equation.

29. $|y| = 8$

30. $-x = 12$

31. $6x = 32$

32. $24 = 3y - 6$

33. $\frac{n}{6} = 18$

34. $\frac{2}{3}t + 5 = 35$

35. $-6y - 1.5 = -21$

36. $0.45 = -0.6a - 0.3$

Find the volume of each figure.

37. A cylinder with radius 6.5 cm and height 12 cm.

38. A rectangular prism 12 in. long, 11 in. wide, and 9 in. high.

Mid-Year Test

For use after Modules 1–4

For Questions 39–45, use the stem-and-leaf plot of test scores.

39. Find the mean.

40. Find the median.

41. Find the mode.

42. Which average from Exercises 39–41 do you think best represents the data set? Explain your reasoning.

Test Scores

6	2 2 3 4 4 5 7
7	4 5 5 7 8 9
8	0 0 1 1 3 4 4 5
9	0 0 0 2 2 4 6

7 | 5 means 75

43. Give the range, lower extreme, upper extreme, lower quartile, and upper quartile for the data.

44. Construct a box-and-whisker plot for the data.

45. What percent of the data is represented by the box from the box-and-whisker plot?

For Questions 46 and 47, write each underlined number in scientific notation.

46. The average distance from the sun to the earth is approximately 150,000,000 kilometers.

47. It is believed that the moon is more than 4,500,000,000 years old.

48. Two number cubes with sides numbered 1 through 6 are rolled. Find the theoretical probability of rolling a sum of 10.

49. In the circle graph at the right, what percent of Sophie's fruit punch is lemonade? How do you know?

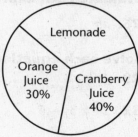

Sophie's Fruit Punch

Lemonade

Orange Juice 30%

Cranberry Juice 40%

Combine like terms to simplify each expression.

50. $3x + 4x$

51. $3y^2 + y^2$

52. $5m - m + 2 + 7$

53. In the Venn diagram at the right, how many students have brothers and sisters?

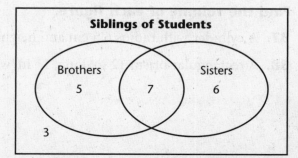

Siblings of Students

Brothers   5   7   Sisters   6

3

Mid-Year Test
For use after Modules 1–4

For Questions 54 and 55, graph each equation. Tell whether the graph is *linear* or *nonlinear*.

54. $y = 2x + 4$

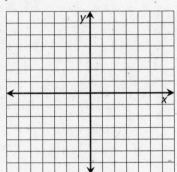

55. $y = x^2 - 2$

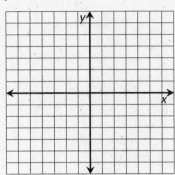

56. The flagpole in the diagram below is 15 feet tall and is used to measure the height of the tree. Find the height of the tree.

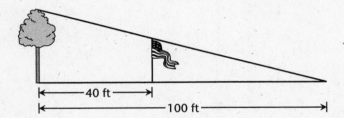

For Questions 57 and 58, tell whether the given rates are equivalent.

57. 90 words/min; 2 words/sec

58. 730 apples/year; 2 apples/day

59. Make a tree diagram that shows all the possible outcomes of three flips of a coin. What is the theoretical probability of flipping all heads?

60. Find the slope of a line that passes through $(0, 4)$ and $(1, 2)$.

61. Write an equation in slope-intercept form for the line through the points $(0, 3)$ and $(3, 0)$.

For Questions 62–64, write each rational number as a terminating or repeating decimal.

62. $1\frac{1}{4}$

63. $\frac{7}{15}$

64. $\frac{3}{11}$

65. Find the number of permutations of the letters in the word PATH.

MODULE 3

Diagnostic Test (p. 3-2)

1. −60; exact
2. $\frac{5}{6}$; exact
3. 8.8; estimate
4. C
5.

6. D
7. B
8. D
9. C
10. $5.87 \cdot 10^6$
11. 6,945,000,000
12. 5.71
13. 15.75
14. **a.** 29 students **b.** 61 students
    c. 32 students **d.** 15 students

SECTION 1

Practice and Applications (p. 3-9)

1. 8
2. −9
3. 50
4. 0.1
5. $\frac{6}{7}$
6. −4000
7. **a.** 1904 cm^2 **b.** about 43.6 cm by 43.6 cm
8. **a.** 78 yd **b.** 252 yd^2 **c.** 648 yd^2
9. 6.5
10. 8.4
11. 2.8
12. 12.2
13. 6.4 in.

14. any number between 144 and 169
15. $\frac{7}{54}$
16. 5 and 7
17. Answers may vary.
18. **a.**

4920 Btu/hr; 4400 Btu/hr
b. Yes; because the capacity needed for the two rooms is 9320 Btu's, the amount required is less than 10,000 Btu's.

19. **a.**

b. No; Sample Response: because the larger room needs a capacity of 7680 Btu/hr and the smaller room needs a capacity of 4170 Btu/hr, which is not half of 7680 Btu/hr.

20. **a.** 8640 in.^{3} **b.** Answers may vary.
    c. Sample Response: about 20.5 in. by 20.5 in. by 20.5 in.
21. **a.** 4096 in.^{3}; 4096 in.^{3} **b.** cube: 1536 in.^{2}; prism: 1792 in.^{2} **c.** The amount of cardboard needed to make a cubical box is less than the amount of cardboard needed to make a second box with the same volume but different dimensions.

Study Guide Exercises (p. 3-13)

1. 600
2. −8
3. $\frac{1}{5}$
4. 0.2
5. 0.009
6. 70
7. 0.03
8. $\frac{3}{4}$

9. about 6.1
10. about 4.9
11. about 12.0
12. about 11.5
13. about 10.1
14. about 15.1
15. about 5.9
16. about 1.4
17. 0.05; exact
18. about 6; estimate
19. −30; exact
20. 729 cm^3
21. **a.** 4 times **b.** 8 times **c.** 132 in.; 66 in.

Quick Quiz (p. 3-14)

1. 6
2. −10
3. 6.9
4. 3.7
5. about 37.4 ft by 37.4 ft

SECTION 2

Practice and Applications (p. 3-17)

1. 6
2. 9
3. 6
4. 22.91
5. −1
6. 1.39
7. 6
8. $-\dfrac{5}{32}$
9. about 13.4
10. about 16.5
11. **a.** 2.41 **b.** No; Sample Response: 2.41 is not close to 1. **c.** 1; Sample Response: Yes; for a circular lake, $A = \pi r^2$ and $L = 2\pi r$, so $\dfrac{L}{\sqrt{2\pi \cdot \pi r^2}} = 1$.
12. 5

13. 7
14. −21.33
15. −0.17
16. −12.5
17. −1.33
18. Answers may vary.
19. **a.** 37.5 ft **b.** about 53.3 mi/hr
20. **a.** about 22.1 mi/hr
    b.
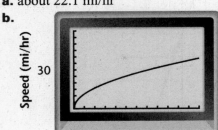
    c. 35 mi/hr
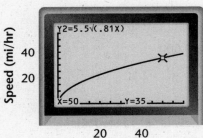

21.

22.

MODULE 3

Answer Key

For use with Module 3

23.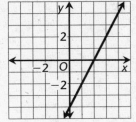

24.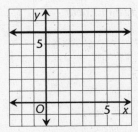

25.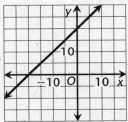

26.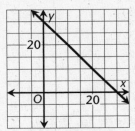

27. 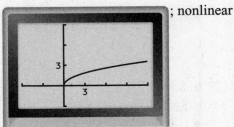 ; nonlinear

28. 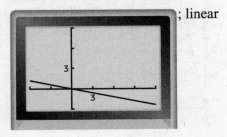 ; linear

29. 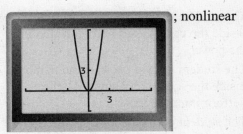 ; nonlinear

30. 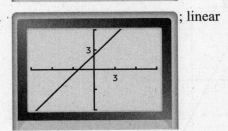 ; nonlinear

31. 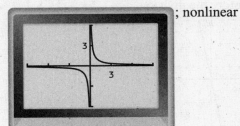 ; linear

32. 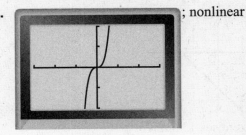 ; nonlinear

Study Guide Exercises (p. 3-21)

1. 2
2. 14
3. 0.85
4. 72.11
5. 18
6. 0.71
7. 1.3
8. 0.67
9. −4.43
10. The student performed the addition before the multiplication.

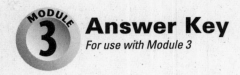

11. The student did not perform the addition inside the parentheses before evaluating the power.

12. The student did not subtract the numbers inside the square root symbol before performing the square root.

13. The student performed the subtraction before the division.

14.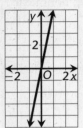

15.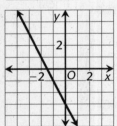

16.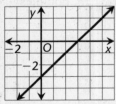

17. Exercises 15 and 16

18. Exercise 14

19. Exercise 16

20. 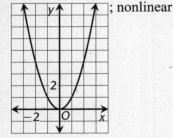 ; nonlinear

21. 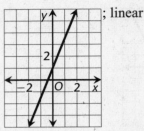 ; linear

22. 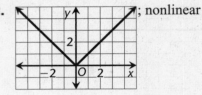 ; nonlinear

Quick Quiz (p. 3-22)

1. 2.67

2. −4

3. 1.73

4.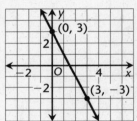

5. nonlinear

SECTION 3

Practice and Applications (p. 3-25)

1. 2

2. $\frac{1}{2}$

3. $\frac{1}{4}$

4. **a.** 8.5 **b.** 8.5 **c.** $y = 8.5x$

5. **a.** $y = 9.35x$ **b.** slope = 9.35;

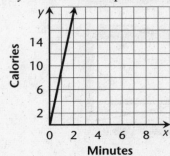

Answer Key

For use with Module 3

6. a.

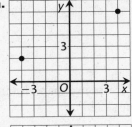

b.

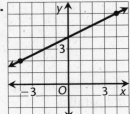

c. $\frac{1}{2}$

d. Sample Response: Connect the points with a line; count the number of units straight up from $(-4, 2)$ and over to $(4, 6)$. Find the quotient; $\frac{4}{8} = \frac{1}{2}$.

7. $-\frac{2}{3}$

8. B; The line crosses the y-axis at $(0, 0)$.

9. A; The line crosses the y-axis at $(0, -4)$.

10. C; The line crosses the y-axis at $(0, 4)$.

11. Sample Response: As a person gets one year older, the remaining life expectancy goes down by one year.

12. a.

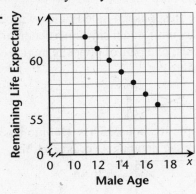

b. The slope is about -1.

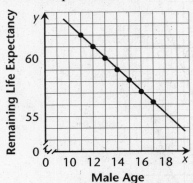

c. $y = 73 - x$, where x is the current age and y is the remaining years **d.** 52

e. Sample Response: slightly off, but very close

Study Guide Exercises (p. 3-28)

1. -1

2. $\frac{4}{5}$

3. a. 45 **b.** $y = 45x$ **c.** $y = 47.25x$

4. Sample Response: 3 hits

5. 2

6. C

Quick Quiz (p. 3-29)

1. 3

2. B; passes through the origin

3. A; passes through $(0, 3)$

4. C; passes through $(0, -3)$

Mid-Module Quiz (p. 3-30)

1. 0.5; exact

2. 20; exact

3. about -11; estimate

4. Sample Response: The volume of the larger cube is 27 cm^3, not 9 cm^3. She is comparing area, not volume.

5. 14

6. $\frac{3}{4}$ or 0.75

Answer Key

For use with Module 3

7. 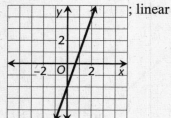 ; linear

8. 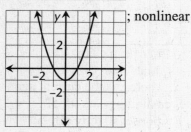 ; nonlinear

9. $\frac{1}{2}$

10. −2

11. **a.** I **b.** about 307,000,000

SECTION 4
Practice and Applications (p. 3-36)

1. $\frac{4}{3}$

2. **a.** *S* **b.** *ST*

3. **a.** 40° **b.** 110° **c.** 8

4. △*RST* is similar to △*UVT*.

5. *ABCD* is similar to *IHKJ*.

6. Sample Response:

These figures have the same angle measures, but are not similar.

7. **a.** about 9593 feet **b.** The triangles are similar because two pairs of corresponding angles are equal in measure.

8.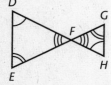

9. **a.**

b. square; Sample Response: paperfolding or measure the four sides

10. **a.**

b. No; it is not a parallelogram because the opposite sides are not parallel.

c.

Sample Response: Each triangle is a right triangle. **d.** ∠*BAD* and ∠*BCD*

11. Sample Response:

Answers may vary.

12. Sample Response: 4-sided figure with 2 pairs of consecutive equal sides; perpendicular diagonals; one pair of opposite angles equal in measure

13. **a.**

b. Sample Response: They seem to be equal; measure the diagonals. **c.** No. **d.** Yes.

e.

square

Answer Key

For use with Module 3

14. a.

b. Sample Response: The diagonals are not equal; measure the diagonals.
c. No. **d.** Yes.
e.

four sides equal (known as a "rhombus")

15. a.

b. all sides equal; equilateral
c.

They have the same center.

Study Guide Exercises (p. 3-40)

1. 2 : 5 or 5 : 2
2. **a.** EC **b.** $\frac{BC}{DC} = \frac{AC}{EC}$ or $\frac{BC}{AC} = \frac{DC}{EC}$
3. **a.** 37° **b.** 6 cm **c.** 25 cm
4. $\triangle ABC$ is similar to $\triangle EFD$.
5. $JKLM$ is similar to $TQRS$.
6. Check students' work.
7. **a.**

b. square **c.**

Sample Response: The resulting rectangle is also a square.

Quick Quiz (p. 3-41)

1. $\frac{5}{3}$
2. $m\angle F$

3. 7.2
4. $\frac{3}{2}$ or 1.5

SECTION 5

Practice and Applications (p. 3-44)

1. 18,600,000,000
2. 780,000,000
3. 65,000,000
4. 602,000,000,000,000,000,000,000
5. A, C
6. Alpha Centauri, Rigil Kentaurus; $2.5284 \cdot 10^{13}$ mi
7. Altair; $9.702 \cdot 10^{13}$ mi
8. **a.** 1,320,000,000
   b. 1,450,000,000; $1\frac{1}{10}$ times as much
9. 15
10. 33.75
11. 1.28
12. 9
13. 21.76
14. 0.74
15. 0
16. 1
17. −7
18. −2
19. −8.6
20. −18
21. **a.** 420.5 Cal **b.** about 630
    c. Sample Response: a little over 3 hours
22. about $130
23. about $125
24. 12 weeks
25. No; Carol always has more money.

Study Guide Exercises (p. 3-47)

1. $4.87 \cdot 10^6$
2. $3 \cdot 10^2$
3. $1.02 \cdot 10^{11}$
4. $1.2 \cdot 10^9$
5. $8.9023 \cdot 10^8$

6. $1.6 \cdot 10^{13}$
7. 19,000
8. 309,800
9. 8000
10. 7100
11. 352,000,000
12. 1,580,000
13. **a.** 2,920,000; 2.92×10^6; 1,720,000; 1.72×10^6 **b.** about 1.7 times more
14. $m = 2.8$
15. $y = -56.95$
16. $w = 18.5$
17. $t = 0.21$
18. **a.** $90 **b.** $86 **c.** 80 hr

Quick Quiz (p. 3-48)

1. 2×10^6; 1.55×10^6
2. 5
3. 155
4. -0.144

SECTION 6

Practice and Applications (p. 3-51)

1. inclusive
2. inclusive
3. exclusive
4. 18
5. 6
6. 40
7. Sample Response: Add 1 to the 6.
8. argali, leopard, iguana, chimpanzee, green sea turtle
9. about 1%

Study Guide Exercises (p. 3-53)

1. chocolate
2. 16 students
3. 9 students

4. 10 students
5. 35 students
6. 26
7. 6
8. 8
9. Ty Baker and Ron Ito
10. 5
11. 8

Quick Quiz (p. 3-54)

1. 8 skaters
2. Eric Heiden
3. 14 skaters

END-OF-MODULE RESOURCES AND ASSESSMENTS

Practice and Applications, Sections 1–6 (p. 3-55)

1. -11
2. 0.03
3. $\frac{1}{7}$
4. -0.25
5. about -5.2
6. about 4.5
7. about 0.6
8. about -6.1
9. between 8 and 9
10. **a.** 13 m **b.** It is multiplied by 9.
11. $11\frac{2}{3}$
12. 20
13. $2\frac{1}{3}$
14. 5
15. No.
16. No.
17. Yes.
18. No.

For use with Module 3

19.

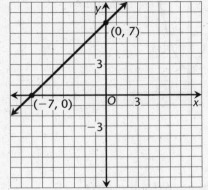

24. 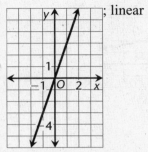 ; linear

20.

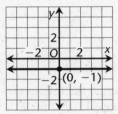

25.

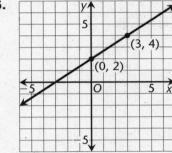

slope $= \frac{2}{3}$

21.

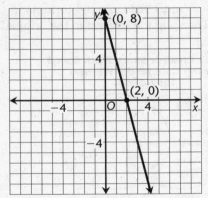

26.

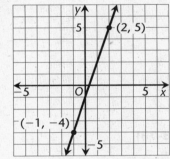

slope $= 3$

22. ; linear

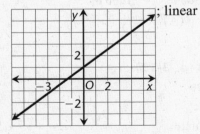

27.

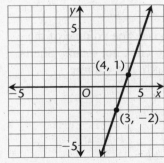

slope $= 3$

23. ; nonlinear

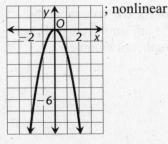

28.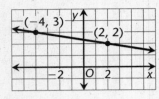

slope $= -\frac{1}{6}$

29. $17\frac{1}{3}$ ft

30. 8.5 ft

31–33. Check students' work.

34. $8 \cdot 10^2$

35. $2.3 \cdot 10^7$

36. $3.678 \cdot 10^3$

37. $x = 25$

38. $f = 74.64$

39. $g = -18.75$

40. $y = -396$

41. $y = -6.4$

42. $f = 0.5$

43. $x = 3.7$

44. $x = 0.01$

45. 12 students

46. 5 students

47. 20 students

Test Form A (p. 3-73)

1. 0.6; exact

2. 100; exact

3. 9.2; estimate

4. Sample Response: The volume of the larger box is 16 cm^3, not 4 cm^3. She is comparing length, not volume.

5. 28

6. $\frac{6}{5}$ or $1\frac{1}{5}$

7. 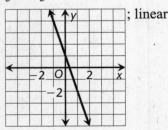 ; linear

8. 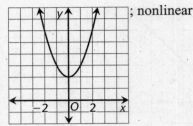 ; nonlinear

9. -2

10. 1

11. 25 ft

12. a. III b. 66,000 subscribers

13. $7.578 \cdot 10^7$

14. $6.602 \cdot 10^9$

15. 148,000,000 km^2

16. $42,200,000,000

17. Sample Response: Change the rate to a decimal, 0.05; substitute $150.50 for P, 0.05 for r, and 1 for t into the formula to find I. Then add the interest to the original principal.

18.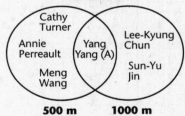

19. Yang Yang (A)

20. 6 skaters

Test Form B (p. 3-75)

1. 0.1; exact

2. -30; exact

3. 7.9; estimate

4. Sample Response: The volume of the larger box is 54 cm^3, not 6 cm^3. He is comparing length, not volume.

5. 16

6. $\frac{7}{5}$ or $1\frac{2}{5}$

MODULE 3 Answer Key

For use with Module 3

7. 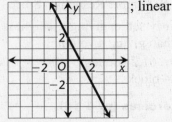 ; linear

8. 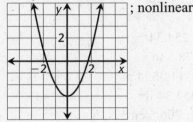 ; nonlinear

9. $\frac{1}{2}$

10. -1

11. 12 ft

12. **a.** III **b.** 1,267,000,000 people

13. $2.15 \cdot 10^6$

14. $7.8 \cdot 10^7$

15. $10,240,000,000,000

16. 15,400,000 people

17. Substitute 15 for h in the formula to find p.

18. **Men's Olympic Slalom and Giant Slalom Gold Medal Winners 1988–2006**

19. Alberto Tomba and Benjamin Raich

20. 9 skiers

Standardized Test (p. 3-77)

1. c

2. b

3. c

4. b

5. d

6. a

7. d

8. a

9. a

10. c

11. d

12. c

Performance Assessment (p. 3-78)

1. right scalene triangle

2. line AC: $y = x - 10$ (Equation 4)
line BC: $7y = x + 14$ (Equation 1)
line AB: $y = -x + 2$ (Equation 2)

3. 1

4.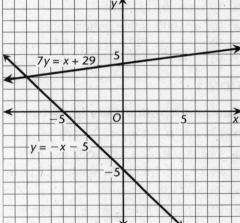

5. Answers may vary, but should not include the line $y = x - 1$. The line $y = x - 1$ forms a congruent triangle. All other lines with a slope of 1 will form a similar triangle.

6. 1

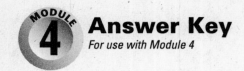

MODULE 4

Diagnostic Test (p. 4-2)

1. B
2. C
3. C
4. $\frac{S.A.}{V} = \frac{13}{30} = 0.4\overline{3}$ or $\frac{S.A.}{V} = \frac{979.68}{2260.8} \approx 0.43$
5. slope $= -\frac{3}{2}$; y-intercept $= 1$; $y = -\frac{3}{2}x + 1$
6. slope $= 0$; y-intercept $= 2$; $y = 2$
7. $\frac{5}{8}$, $0.62\overline{5}$, 0.63, $\frac{19}{30}$, $0.\overline{63}$
8. $x = \frac{200}{3}$ or $66\frac{2}{3}$
9. $x = 28$
10. **a.** 30 ways **b.** 15 ways
11. **a.** 10^3 or 1000 authorization codes
    b. $\frac{10^2}{10^3} = \frac{1}{10}$ **c.** $\frac{720}{1000} = \frac{18}{25}$ **d.** $\frac{9}{10}$

SECTION 1

Practice and Applications (p. 4-10)

1. **a.** 15π cm **b.** 8π in. **c.** 2.3π m
2. **a.** 47.1 cm **b.** 25.12 in. **c.** 7.222 m
3. **a.** 94.2 in. or 7.85 ft **b.** about 39.5 turns
4. about 61.75 ft
5. **a.** 121π ft^2 **b.** 100π cm^2 **c.** 12.25π in.^{2}
6. **a.** 379.94 ft^2 **b.** 314 cm^2 **c.** 38.465 in.^{2}
7. **a.** 78.5 in.^{2} **b.** 235.5 in.^{2} **c.** 28.26 in.^{2}
   d. about $\frac{1}{8}$
8. **a.** 125 cm^3 **b.** 100.48 in.^{3} **c.** 36 ft^3
9. 602.88 cm^3
10. 441.5 cm^3
11. 10,173.6 cm^3
12. 2592 cm^3
13. 378 cm^3
14. 750 cm^3
15. $36,000\pi$ in.^{3}
16. 98.784π m^3
17. 288π ft^3

18. **a.** $272\frac{1}{4}$ in.^{3} **b.** Sample Response: Since the contents may settle, giving a weight is more useful than giving a volume.
19. **a.** 565.5 ft^3 **b.** 61.2 pounds
    c. about 122.4 blocks

Study Guide Exercises (p. 4-14)

1. about 80.384 cm
2. 5 turns
3. 81π cm^2; 254.34 cm^2
4. 25π in.^{2}; 78.5 in.^{2}
5. 3.61π m^2; 11.3354 m^2
6. 81π ft^2; 254.34 ft^2
7. 225π cm^2; 706.5 cm^2
8. 9π in.^{2}; 28.26 in.^{2}
9. 1.96π m^2; 6.1544 m^2
10. 16π ft^2; 50.24 ft^2
11. 49π cm^2; 153.86 cm^2
12. about 353.25 mm^3
13. 48 m^3
14. about 82.4 cm^3
15. 512π cm^3 or about 1608 cm^3
16. 99π cm^3 or about 311 cm^3
17. 1296π cm^3 or about 4069 cm^3
18. 1014 cm^3
19. 600 cm^3
20. 90 cm^3
21. $6550\frac{2}{3}\pi$ ft^3; 20,569.09$\overline{3}$ ft^3
22. 121.5π in.^{3}; 381.51 in.^{3}
23. 4.5π m^3; 14.13 m^3

Quick Quiz (p. 4-15)

1. 75.36 cm
2. 156.25π in.^{2}
3. **a.** 282.6 ft^3 **b.** 945 cm^3 **c.** 2143.6 m^3
4. Sample Response: Each boy receives the same volume of soup, but Tobin's bowl has a larger diameter opening than Mac's cup; therefore, the area of the circle exposed to the air is greater in Tobin's bowl, making his soup cool off faster.

Answer Key

For use with Module 4

SECTION 2

Practice and Applications (p. 4-18)

1. 251.2 cm^2
2. 12.56 m^2
3. 25.12 ft^2
4. 122.1 m^2
5. 292.3 cm^2
6. 502.4 ft^2
7. 3768 ft^2
8. 54.2 in.^2
9. 311.3 cm^2
10. 192.325 in.^2
11. 26.7 in.^2
12. $\frac{1}{2} \text{ cm}$
13. about 1.83
14. about 0.83
15. about 0.43
16. 15; 14, 13
17. about 0.963
18. about 1.29
19. about 1.81
20. **a.** the 19 ounce soup can; $1.74 < 2.12$
    b. about 0.55 **c.** higher; $\frac{10}{19} = 0.53$
    d. lower; $\frac{2.5}{3} = 0.8\overline{3}$ **e.** Sample Response:
    the 19 ounce soup can because the ratios
    come out better in all cases and it will cost
    less to manufacture for a given amount
    of soup

Study Guide Exercises (p. 4-22)

1. 150.8 ft^2
2. 678.59 mm^2
3. 34.68 cm^2
4. 706.36 yd^2
5. 2612.5 m^2
6. $21{,}352.28 \text{ ft}^2$
7. about 66 ft^2
8. 2.67
9. 4.4

10. 0.8
11. 1.1
12. 0.8
13. 0.9
14. **a.** salmon: 1; tomato paste: about 1.04; corn:
    about 0.75 **b.** corn, salmon, tomato paste

Quick Quiz (p. 4-23)

1. 753.6 cm^2
2. $\frac{2}{3}$
3. Sample Response: $r = 10 \text{ cm}$, $h = 4.33 \text{ cm}$

SECTION 3

Practice and Applications (p. 4-29)

1. $\frac{3}{5}$ **2.** -2 **3.** 0
4. $-\frac{7}{2}$ **5.** 0 **6.** $\frac{3}{8}$
7. undefined **8.** 0 **9.** undefined
10. **a.** C **b.** D **c.** A **d.** B
11. about 0.7% per year **12.** 0
13. 0.32% per year **14.** $y = -\frac{3}{2}x + 3$
15. $y = \frac{1}{3}x$ **16.** $y = -\frac{1}{2}x + 1$
17. $y = -2x + 6$ **18.** $y = \frac{3}{2}x + 3$
19. $y = 5$ **20.** $y = -2x + 8$
21. $y = 0.4x + 5.8$ **22.** $y = \frac{5}{4}x + 5$
23. **a.** slope 2.86; y-intercept $(0, 249)$; The slope
    is the rate of increase in the U.S. population
    per year, 2,580,000; the y-intercept gives the
    population in the year 0 (or 1990).
    b. $y = 2.86x + 249$ **c.** 360,000,000
    d. very close
24.

slope = 0

25.

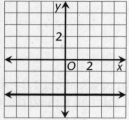

slope = 0

26.

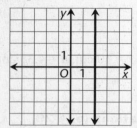

Slope is undefined.

27.

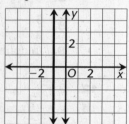

Slope is undefined.

Study Guide Exercises (p. 4-33)

1. 1

2. $-\frac{1}{11}$

3. $-\frac{9}{4}$

4. zero

5. $-\frac{2}{3}$

6. undefined

7. B

8. C

9. D

10. $y = \frac{3}{4}x - 3$

11. $y = -3$

12. $y = -\frac{5}{7}x + 1\frac{1}{7}$

13. $y = \frac{2}{3}x + 3\frac{1}{3}$

14. $y = -x + 3$

15. $y = x$

16.

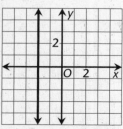

Slope is undefined.

17.

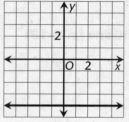

slope = 0

18.

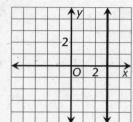

Slope is undefined.

Quick Quiz (p. 4-34)

1. $y = 3x + 5$

2. 3; each term increases by 3.

3. 5; it is the constant.

4. Sample Response: $y = 3x + 2$

5. True; To calculate the slope, you would have to divide the rise by 0 (the run) and division by zero is undefined.

Mid-Module Quiz (p. 4-35)

1. the square prism; Sample Response: The objects have the same dimensions, so the cylinder will fit inside the prism, leaving additional space at each corner of the prism.

2. A

3. **a.** 15π ft

   b. Sample Response: Substitute 3.14 for π. $C = 15\pi \approx 15 \cdot 3.14 = 47.1$ ft

4. 226.08 cm^2

5. $\frac{S.A.}{V} = \frac{6\pi(6) + 2(3^2\pi)}{3^2\pi(6)} = \frac{54\pi}{54\pi} = \frac{1}{1}$

6. slope $= -\frac{3}{5}$; y-intercept $= -1$; $y = -\frac{3}{5}x - 1$

7. slope $= 2$; y-intercept $= 0$; $y = 2x$

8. slope $= 0$; y-intercept $= -1$; $y = -1$

Answer Key
For use with Module 4

SECTION 4

Practice and Applications (p. 4-37)

1. $\frac{2}{5}$ 2. $\frac{6}{1}$ 3. $\frac{5}{8}$

4. $\frac{7}{2}$ 5. $\frac{17}{2}$ 6. $\frac{1}{2}$

7. $0.58\overline{3}$ 8. $0.\overline{6}$ 9. 10

10. $0.\overline{2}$ 11. 7.75   12. 0.75

13. **a.** $0.19\overline{4}$ **b.** 0.25 **c.** $-2.\overline{3}$; $-2.\overline{3}$, $0.19\overline{4}$, 0.25

14. **a.** 6 **b.** Sample Response: $\frac{1}{14}$

15. **a.** $0.1\overline{54}$; $0.15\overline{4}$; $0.\overline{154}$; $0.\overline{15}$; Sample Response: Expand the decimals further until they can be compared.
b. $2.\overline{3}$; $2.33\overline{2}$; $2.\overline{32}$; $2.3\overline{2}$; Sample Response: Expand the decimals further until they can be compared.

16. 27   17. 16   18. 62.5

19. $10.\overline{6}$ 20. 120   21. $8.\overline{72}$

22. 1   23. 0   24. $\frac{5}{9}$

25. 10   26. -20 27. $-1\frac{1}{5}$

28. $-1\frac{1}{2}$ 29. -9 30. $-9\frac{5}{12}$

31. **a.** $P = 2.2K$, where P is the number of pounds and K is the number of kilograms. **b.** 39.6 lb **c.** $6.\overline{36}$ kilograms

32. **a.** 23.544 yd^3 **b.** about 15.3 m^3

Study Guide Exercises (p. 4-41)

1. $-\frac{2}{1}$ 2. $\frac{25}{6}$ 3. $\frac{1}{5}$

4. $\frac{3}{8}$ 5. $-\frac{5}{4}$ 6. $\frac{7}{1}$

7. $0.41\overline{6}$ 8. $-2.\overline{1}$ 9. 1.6

10. 0.92   11. $-5.\overline{18}$ 12. 1.75

13. $-5.\overline{18}$, $-2.\overline{1}$, $0.41\overline{6}$, 0.92, 1.6, 1.75

14. $x = -15$ 15. $m = -5\frac{1}{3}$ 16. $y = \frac{5}{8}$

17. $t = \frac{2}{7}$ 18. $r = 104$ 19. $f = 151\frac{1}{4}$

20. $x = 9$ 21. $x = 1.1$ 22. $x = -11\frac{1}{4}$

23. **a.** $i = 0.39c$, where i = the number of inches and c = the number of centimeters. **b.** 154 **c.** 49 **d.** Divide the number of inches by 0.39.

Quick Quiz (p. 4-42)

1. D   2. $3.\overline{6}$ 3. 0.375

4. $-\frac{6}{5}$ or $-1\frac{1}{5}$ 5. $\frac{12}{5}$ or $2\frac{2}{5}$ 6. -62

7. -2 8. $-\frac{1}{4}$ 9. -26

SECTION 5

Practice and Applications (p. 4-47)

1. **a.**

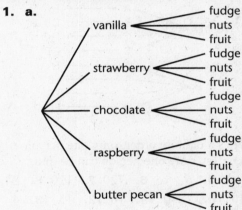

   b. 15

2. 12   3. 3,628,800   4. 2

5. 720   6. 24   7. 120

8. 6   9. 40,320   10. 24

11. 479,001,600   12. 3,628,800 ways

13. 5040   14. 362,880   15. 15

16. **a.** 5 **b.** 10 **c.** 10 **d.** 5 **e.** 1 **f.** 16

17. 10

18. **a.** 28 **b.** 56 **c.** 28

19. 66

20. **a.** 5 **b.** 24

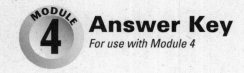

Answer Key
For use with Module 4

Study Guide Exercises (p. 4-51)

1.

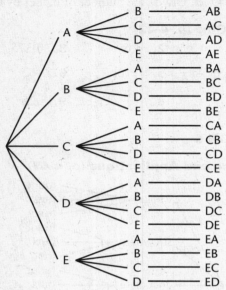

1st	2nd	Arrangement
A	B	AB
	C	AC
	D	AD
	E	AE
B	A	BA
	C	BC
	D	BD
	E	BE
C	A	CA
	B	CB
	D	CD
	E	CE
D	A	DA
	B	DB
	C	DC
	E	DE
E	A	EA
	B	EB
	C	EC
	D	ED

2. 20

3. There's a definite order; only one person can be 1st, only one person can be 2nd.

4. 2 **5.** 6 **6.** 720 **7.** 120 **8.** 24

9. 5040 **10.** 3840 **11.** 10 **12.** 15 **13.** 4

14. Order is not important as long as there are the correct number in each group and they are different.

15. **a.** 4 **b.** 6 **c.** 4 **d.** 11

Quick Quiz (p. 4-52)

1. 96 ways

2. 720 ways

3. 56 combinations

SECTION 6

Practice and Applications (p. 4-54)

1.

1, 1	1, 2	1, 3	1, 4	1, 5	1, 6
2, 1	2, 2	2, 3	2, 4	2, 5	2, 6
3, 1	3, 2	3, 3	3, 4	3, 5	3, 6
4, 1	4, 2	4, 3	4, 4	4, 5	4, 6
5, 1	5, 2	5, 3	5, 4	5, 5	5, 6
6, 1	6, 2	6, 3	6, 4	6, 5	6, 6

2. $\frac{25}{36}, \frac{10}{36}, \frac{1}{36}$ 3. $\frac{11}{36}$

4. **a.** 10,000 **b.** $\frac{2000}{10,000} = \frac{1}{5}$ **c.** $\frac{100}{10,000} = \frac{1}{100}$

   d. 0 **e.** $10^7 = 10,000,000$

5. **a.** 36 **b.** 4; 3 **c.** $\frac{7}{36}$

6. **a, b.** Answers may vary.

Study Guide Exercises (p. 4-56)

1. 36

First number cube	Second number cube	Outcome
1	1	1, 1
	2	1, 2
	3	1, 3
	4	1, 4
	5	1, 5
	6	1, 6
2	1	2, 1
	2	2, 2
	3	2, 3
	4	2, 4
	5	2, 5
	6	2, 6
3	1	3, 1
	2	3, 2
	3	3, 3
	4	3, 4
	5	3, 5
	6	3, 6
4	1	4, 1
	2	4, 2
	3	4, 3
	4	4, 4
	5	4, 5
	6	4, 6
5	1	5, 1
	2	5, 2
	3	5, 3
	4	5, 4
	5	5, 5
	6	5, 6
6	1	6, 1
	2	6, 2
	3	6, 3
	4	6, 4
	5	6, 5
	6	6, 6

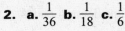

Answer Key

For use with Module 4

2. a. $\frac{1}{36}$ b. $\frac{1}{18}$ c. $\frac{1}{6}$

3. $\frac{11}{36}$ 　　4. $\frac{1}{4}$ 　　5. $\frac{1}{125}$

6. $\frac{8}{125}$ 　　7. $\frac{27}{125}$ 　　8. $\frac{64}{125}$

9. 0 　　　　　　10. 1

11. 160,000 　　　12. 160,000

13. $\frac{1}{12}$

Quick Quiz (p. 4-57)

1. HH, HT, TH, TT

2. a. $\frac{1}{4}$ b. $\frac{1}{2}$ c. $\frac{1}{4}$

3. $\frac{3}{4}$

4. 10^5 or 100,000 codes

5. $\frac{10,000}{100,000} = \frac{1}{10}$

END-OF-MODULE RESOURCES AND ASSESSMENTS

Practice and Applications, Sections 1–6 (p. 4-58)

1. about 14.62 mm

2. 11 cm

3. about 471.24 mm^3

4. about 40.26 in.^{3}

5. about 339.29 ft^3

6. 1004.8 in.^{2}

7. S.A. = 384 mm^2; V = 512 mm^3

8. 150.72 in.^{2}

9. slope: –3; y-intercept: 8

10. $y = 5x + 4$

11. $y = -3x - 2$

12. slope = –3

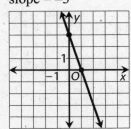

13. slope = 3

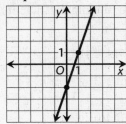

14. slope = $\frac{1}{2}$

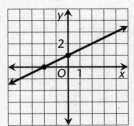

15. –28 　　16. $137\frac{1}{2}$ 　　17. –22

18. $0.\overline{63}$ 　　19. 3.8 　　20. $-0.8\overline{3}$

21. $\frac{1}{3}; \frac{2}{3}$

22. Combinations; the order in which the kinds of flowers are chosen doesn't matter.

23. 10 　　　24. $\frac{1}{1296} \approx 0.00077$

25. $\frac{1}{16} = 0.0625$ 　　26. $\frac{5}{18} \approx 0.28$

27. $\frac{1}{81} \approx 0.0123$ 　　28. $\frac{625}{1296} \approx 0.48$

29. $\frac{1}{81} \approx 0.0123$

Test Form A (p. 4-61)

1. 251.2 in.^{2}

2. 216.0948 cm^2

3. $\frac{S.A.}{V} = \frac{326.56}{452.16} \approx 0.72$

4. $\frac{S.A.}{V} = \frac{244.92}{282.6} \approx 0.87$

5. Sample Response: No. π is a factor of both the numerator and the denominator of the ratio, so the the ratio in Question 3 would be $\frac{104\pi}{144\pi} = \frac{104}{144} = \frac{13}{18} = 0.7\overline{2}$.

Answer Key

For use with Module 4

6. The can in Question 3 is more efficient. The smaller the ratio, the more efficient the can is.

7. slope $= -\frac{2}{3}$; y-intercept $= 1$; $y = -\frac{2}{3}x + 1$

8. slope $= \frac{5}{2}$; y-intercept $= 3$; $y = \frac{5}{2}x + 3$

9. $0.72\overline{5}$, $\frac{3}{4}$, 0.752, $0.\overline{75}$, $\frac{13}{16}$

10. $x = \frac{32}{3}$ or $10\frac{2}{3}$

11. $x = -2$

12. **a.** 120 different uniforms **b.** 24 ways **c.** 90 combinations

13. **a.** 10^4 or 10,000 identification codes
b. $\frac{1,000}{10,000} = \frac{1}{10}$ **c.** $\frac{10}{10,000} = \frac{1}{1000}$
d. $\frac{100}{10,000} = \frac{1}{100}$

Test Form B (p. 4-63)

1. 207.24 in.^{2}

2. 298.0488 cm^2

3. $\frac{S.A.}{V} = \frac{188.4}{197.82} \approx 0.95$

4. $\frac{S.A.}{V} = \frac{722.2}{1413} \approx 0.51$

5. Sample Response: No. π is a factor of both the numerator and the denominator of the ratio, so the the ratio in Question 3 would be $\frac{60\pi}{63\pi} = \frac{60}{63} = \frac{20}{21} = 0.\overline{952380}$

6. The can in Question 4 is more efficient. The smaller the ratio, the more efficient the can is.

7. slope $= \frac{2}{3}$; y-intercept $= 1$; $y = \frac{2}{3}x + 1$

8. slope $= \frac{1}{3}$; y-intercept $= 0$; $y = \frac{1}{3}x$

9. $\frac{5}{16}$, 0.37, $0.3\overline{7}$, $\frac{3}{8}$, $0.37\overline{5}$

10. $x = \frac{125}{2}$ or $62\frac{1}{2}$

11. $x = -0.9$

12. **a.** 40 ways **b.** 24 ways **c.** 10 combinations

13. **a.** 26^5 or 11,881,376 identification codes
b. $\frac{26^4}{26^5} = \frac{1}{26}$ **c.** $\frac{26}{26^5} = \frac{1}{26^4} = \frac{1}{456,976}$
d. $\frac{26^3}{26^5} = \frac{1}{26^2} = \frac{1}{676}$

Standardized Test (p. 4-65)

1. b   **2.** a   **3.** d
4. b   **5.** b   **6.** c
7. b   **8.** b   **9.** c
10. b   **11.** d   **12.** c

Performance Assessment (p. 4-66)

1.

Height (cm)	Radius (cm)	Area of base (cm²)	Volume (cm³)	Outside Surface area–sides and bottom only (cm²)
3.50	2	12.56	43.96	56.52
3.75	2.2	15.20	57.00	67.03
4.00	2.4	18.09	72.36	78.37
4.25	2.6	21.23	90.23	90.63
4.50	2.8	24.62	110.79	103.73
4.75	3.0	28.26	134.24	117.75
5.00	3.2	32.15	160.75	132.65
5.25	3.4	36.30	190.58	148.39
5.50	3.6	40.69	223.80	165.05
5.75	3.8	45.34	260.71	182.54

2. **a.** The largest nested cup has the least outside surface area to volume ratio. This ratio is $\frac{182.54}{260.71}$ or about 0.70.

b. The outside surface area to volume ratio decreases as the cups get larger.

3. Answers will vary. One possibility is white, yellow, orange, red, pink, purple, blue, green, tan, and black. Students may choose their favorite colors or those they think young children would like.

4. The number of ways to choose the colors is $10 \times 9 \times 8 \times 7 \times 6 \times 5 \times 4 \times 3 \times 2 \times 1 = 3,628,800$.

5. **a.** $P(\text{volume} < 150 \text{ cm}^3) = \frac{6}{10} = 0.60$

b. $P(\text{surface area} < 150 \text{ cm}^2) = \frac{8}{10} = 0.80$

Math Thematics, Book 3
Teacher's Resource Book, Modules 3 and 4

Modules 3 and 4 Cumulative Test (p. CT-1)

1. 0.7; exact

2. -17.3; estimate

3. -8

4. $\frac{3}{2}$ or $1\frac{1}{2}$

5.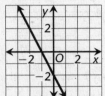

6. B and C

7. **a.** I **b.** 340,000,000 computers

8. $1.148 \cdot 10^8$

9. $2,520,000,000

10. 18 ft

11. 12.6

12. 54

13. 342 cm^2

14. $\frac{7}{15} \approx 0.467$

15. slope $= \frac{3}{2}$; y-intercept $= 2$;
    equation: $y = \frac{3}{2}x + 2$

16. slope $= 0$; y-intercept $= -3$;
    equation: $y = -3$

17. **a.** 36 orders **b.** 15 combinations

18. **a.** 10^4 or 10,000 codes **b.** $\frac{1}{10}$

Answer Key

For use after Modules 1–4

Mid-Year Test (p. MYT-1)

1. –4 **2.** 5   **3.** –6   **4.** $-\frac{1}{6}$
5. $-\frac{11}{20}$ **6.** $2\frac{11}{15}$ **7.** –48 **8.** –72
9. 7 **10.** 6   **11.** –13 **12.** –9
13. 9 **14.** 4   **15.** $\frac{5}{6}$ **16.** $2\frac{1}{4}$
17. 5 **18.** 11
19. 0.8, exact
20. –14.14, estimate
21. 2.5, exact
22. 52.08   **23.** 5%   **24.** 39
25. 150%   **26.** 12   **27.** –6
28. 144   **29.** 8, –8   **30.** –12
31. $5.\overline{3}$, or $5\frac{1}{3}$
32. 10
33. 108
34. 45
35. 3.25
36. –1.25 or $-1\frac{1}{4}$
37. 507π cm^3 or 1592.79 cm^3
38. 1188 in.^{3}
39. 78.8
40. 80
41. 90
42. mean or median, answers may vary
43. range: 34, LE: 62, UE: 96, LQ: 67, UQ: 90
44.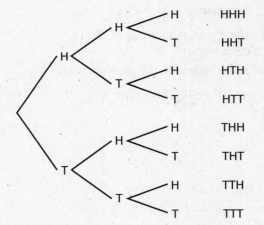
45. 50%
46. 1.5×10^8
47. 4.5×10^9
48. $\frac{1}{12}$
49. 30%; the circle graph represents 100%, so 30% is left after subtracting the percents of orange juice and cranberry juice.
50. $7x$
51. $4y^2$
52. $4m + 9$

53. 7
54. linear

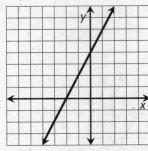

55. nonlinear

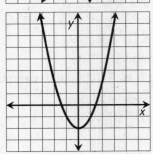

56. 25 ft
57. No.
58. Yes.
59.

First flip	Second flip	Third flip	Outcome
H	H	H	HHH
		T	HHT
	T	H	HTH
		T	HTT
T	H	H	THH
		T	THT
	T	H	TTH
		T	TTT

60. –2
61. $y = -x + 3$
62. 1.25
63. $0.4\overline{6}$
64. $0.\overline{27}$
65. 24